Bust of John Hull Grundy by Mark Batten, past president of the Royal Society of British Sculptors. The bust is in *The British Museum.*

MEDICAL ZOOLOGY FOR TRAVELLERS

Written and illustrated by

JOHN HULL GRUNDY

3rd Edition

with a foreword by
Nicholas Burgess

Published by
Noble Books Ltd.

ISBN 0 906949 00 9

Published by
NOBLE BOOKS LTD.
Watch Cottage, Chilbolton, Hampshire.

Designed and Produced by
Richard Fuller Designs, London
Printed by
PAN LITHO LTD., LONDON

CONTENTS

John Hull Grundy MBE FRES FRSA Lecturer in Entomology, Royal Army Medical College 1945-1967 (opposite).
John Hull Grundy lecturing to students (below).

FOREWORD

John Hull Grundy studied Art at King's College, London, and at the Chelsea School of Art, before joining the staff of the Royal College of Art. There his curriculum included colour design, etching and engraving, fine-line block production and printing. Many of his anatomical studies were carried out at the Royal College of Surgeons and at the Orpington War Hospital.

In 1942 he took up a wartime post at the Royal Army Medical College, Millbank, London, where he remained after the 1939—45 War as Lecturer in Entomology until his retirement at the age of 60 in 1967. A gifted teacher and writer, he established for himself a considerable reputation in his specialism, and his entomological drawings are widely known. However the broader scope of his artistic ability has not perhaps been so fully appreciated, and an exhibition of about 150 diverse examples of his work at the Royal Army Medical College in 1976—77 included anatomical studies, scenes from hospital life, animal drawings and publicity material.

'Medical Zoology for Travellers' is a collection of essays written by John Grundy while in his post as Lecturer at Millbank, and gives ample evidence of the qualities which proved so valuable to his many students, myself amongst them, over the years. These include particularly his ability to convey the essential facts of a subject in an interesting and entertaining manner and the enthusiasm with which he did so, his considerable worldwide knowledge of his subject, and perhaps above all, his particular and unusual skill as an artist. He is a perfectionist in all aspects of his work, and I have known him tear up an apparently perfect and almost completed drawing which was perhaps slightly inaccurate in some small way, rather than present an imperfect result. It almost broke the heart of many a student in his classes to see him rub off the blackboard his most

8

exact and finely executed teaching drawings as if they were insignificant doodles!

The individual quality of Grundy's art work lies in his careful study of subject matter and an appreciation of its potential movement. Many of the drawings in this book are line-drawings, but there are also examples of his particular technique based on the principle of the half-tone screen, where darker areas are obtained by dots or lines touching and running together, and the lighter parts by smaller and more isolated dots.

'Medical Zoology for Travellers' is intended as a book to be read before the journey and referred to on the return, as a stimulus to encourage reference to more detailed works on specific topics, and as a small work of art to give visual enjoyment to the reader. It has been a pleasure to edit the work and to write the captions for the original illustrations.

NRH BURGESS BSc, PhD, FRES, MIBiol.
Lecturer in Entomology,
Royal Army Medical College,
and Ministry of Defence Adviser
in Entomology.

A silver-fish, a primitive wingless insect sometimes found infesting houses, but more common under stones, leaf-mould and even on the sea-shore

Adult cone-nose bug (Vector of American trypanosomiasis or Chagas Disease) with wings spread.

1

THE SIGNIFICANCE, CLASSIFICATION AND DISTRIBUTION OF ARTHROPODS

The value of facts and observations concerning Medical Zoology and Entomology, depend (apart from immediate application to minor and local problems) on their being fitted into a wider, if possible world-wide picture of how they will affect the future. This kind of generalising makes factual work easier to understand and remember by the student, since it trains him to create theories which can be tested against facts and observations. As authority for this method there is Darwin's 'Origin of Species', based on factual observations collected during his 'Voyage of the Beagle'.

It is therefore proposed in this work to outline the subject of Medical Zoology against a background of simple geography and climate, together with such details of habitats and habits as seem appropriate to build a simple picture of the ecology (*oikos*, house) concerning animals which affect the health of man. It is stressed, at this point, that geographical isolation is the main source of the physical differences between animals that have led to the formation of separate species.

In following this technique, the naturalist must obviously spend part of his working time studying living forms, both in the field and vivarium. It is wise, however, before becoming too familiar with the creatures under observation, to consider the possible hazards of medical zoology, or work may be interrupted from time to time by painful accidents.

The following list includes most of the physical retaliations of animals of medical importance. These should be kept in mind, and joined up with any details later found concerning them, particularly when they relate to the safe handling of venomous animals:

1. Fang-bites of large centipedes.
2. Tail-stings of some scorpions.
3. Fang-bites of some spiders.

4. Bites of some ticks.
5. Allergic reactions to some small mites.
6. Bites of some bugs, lice, fleas and flies.
7. Invasion of living tissue by some fly larvae.
8. Burrowing in the skin by jigger fleas.
9. Bites and/or tail stings of some ants, bees, wasps and hornets.
10. Reaction to urticating hairs of some caterpillars.
11. Blistering fluids of some beetles.
12. Venomous bites of two species of lizards, and about three hundred species of poisonous snakes.

Rather more serious than isolated cases of physical attack, however, is the acquirement of arthropod borne disease. The following is a skeleton list of the important diseases caused or transmitted to man by insects and arachnids, together with names of the vectors. The medical entomologist, particularly when he is a field naturalist, must learn to know where these vectors are likely to be found, and must also learn how to avoid or prevent the diseases they cause or transmit. A medical specialist or the appropriate department of a school of tropical medicine will always give advice in answer to specific questions.

DISEASE	VECTOR or CAUSE
DENGUE FEVER .... (virus)	some *Aëdes* mosquitoes
FILARIASIS .... (helminths — tissue nematodes)	some *Aëdes* mosquitoes some *Anopheles* mosquitoes some *Culex* mosquitoes some *Mansonia* mosquitoes some *Culicoides* biting midges some *Simulium* biting blackflies some *Chrysops* biting gadflies
LEISHMANIASIS .... (protozoa — *Leishmania*)	some *Phlebotomus* sandflies
MALARIA .... (protozoa — *Plasmodium*)	some *Anopheles* mosquitoes

MECHANICAL VECTORS ... (of pathogenic bacteria, protozoa, helminth ova, etc.)	all house-frequenting flies which visit filth and human food, e.g. some *Calliphora* bluebottle flies and some *Musca* houseflies
MITE DERMATITIS	*Sarcopes scabiei hominis* human scabies mite, and other mites
MYIASIS Specific myiasis .... (larvae will only develop in or on living tissue)	*Auchmeromyia luteola* Congo floor maggot some *Callitroga* and *Chrysomyia* screw worms. *Cordylobia anthropophaga* tumbu maggot. some *Wohlfahrtia* grey flesh-fly maggots etc.
Semi-specific myiasis .... (larvae usually develop in decaying flesh but may invade wounds)	some *Callitroga* screw-worms some *Lucilia* greenbottle maggots etc.
Accidental myiasis .... (invasion in any stage of alimentary or uro-genital tract)	flies of approximately 20 genera are implicated
PEDICULOSIS.............	*Pediculus humanus* head or body lice *Phthirus pubis* 'crab' or pubic louse
PLAGUE .... (bacillus — *Yersinia pestis*)	all fleas are potential vectors of plague. *Xenopsylla cheopis* is the most important.
RELAPSING FEVER .... *(Borrelia recurrentis)* (spirochaete species)	*Pediculus humanus* head or body louse some *Ornithodorus* soft ticks

RICKETTSIAL FEVERS
(Rickettsiae)

Flea-borne or murine typhus .... some fleas, of which *Xenopsylla* is the most important

Louse-borne typhus .... *Pediculus humanus* head or body lice

Mite-borne typhus (scrub typhus and Japanese river fever) .... some *Trombicula* mite larvae

Tick-borne typhus .... some Ixodidae hard ticks

SANDFLY FEVER .... *Phlebotomus papatasii* sandfly
(virus)

TUNGIASIS .... *Tunga penetrans* jigger flea
(secondary infection)

TRYPANOSOMIASIS
(protozoa — *Trypanosoma)*

(AFRICAN) .... some *Glossina* tsetse flies

(AMERICAN) .... some Triatominae cone-nose bugs

YELLOW FEVER .... *Aedes aegypti* mosquito, also certain other jungle Culicine mosquitoes

It will be noticed on the skeleton list that some vectors which transmitted disease organisms did so by simple mechanical transference on their mouth or body parts.

The majority, however, entered into a complex association with the pathogens, which typically included their incubation over a period of days or weeks within the body of the arthropod, after which transmission to man occurred either by way of the saliva (anterior station infection) or the excreta during blood meals (posterior station infection), or by the release of infective body-fluid when the vector was crushed between the fingers, or by other means, according to the species involved.

An important point not mentioned on the list is that mites and ticks, but not insects, are able to transmit certain disease organisms through their egg stages to succeeding generations.

Before going further with the introduction however, it is necessary to clear up any confusion that may have occurred regarding names and classification.

The words 'arthropod', 'insect', *'Anopheles'*, 'species' and others have already been used without explanation, so that, before a full scale use of more names and terms is indulged in, it is essential briefly to explain their significance and meaning.

In every day practice, each of the myriad living things that are seen around us may be said to belong to a 'Species', for this unit is the basis of taxonomic classification (*taxis,* arrangement; *classis,* assembly). The mosquito seen to bite the back of one's hand belongs to a 'species' — this is made clearer by the Latin derivation of the word, for *specere* simply means "to look". Other differently marked mosquitoes will belong to other species. Those which are obviously closely related, because of similarities that may be described in words, and yet which are obviously not of the same kin, kind; or species, may be grouped together into a Genus (*genos,* begotton race).

Genera which are related may be placed in a "Family" (*familia,* household), and related families may be included in an 'Order'.

Entomologists must be able when given an insect, correctly to place the specimen in its Order, that is, to state whether it is a fly (Order Diptera), a bug (Order Hemiptera), a flea (Order Siphonaptera), and so on.

Orders are gathered into a "Class", and Classes are grouped into a "Phylum" (*phylon,* a nation).

Phyla are placed in a "Kingdom", and there is no classification for living things above the Kingdom Vegetabilia or Plants, and the Kingdom Animalia or Animals.

As taxonomic classification is an artificial invention or filing-system of man, based as it is on observable and recordable relationships between the species, it is often found that the Kingdom, Phylum, Class, Order, Family, Genus, Species groupings do not cover the special characteristics of the species under scrutiny. It is therefore sometimes necessary to subdivide the main or obligate groups by errecting Subkingdoms, Subphyla, Subclasses, Suborders, Subfamilies, Subgeneria and Subspecies. Even these additions are occasionally insufficient to describe a group adequately, so that arbitrary 'Divisions',

'Sections', or 'Series' are introduced where useful.

If it is asked why all these gradings are necessary to the description of a species, the answer is that each grade or heading is a symbol for a large number of constant features, which characteristics would be most uneconomical to repeat each time a differentiation is made between one species and another. A species, for instance, is always given two names, such as *Anopheles maculipennis,* the first being the same as the genus, and always beginning with a capital letter, while the second refers to its specific nature and typically begins with a small initial letter. This binominal wording is invariably printed in *italics,* a usage not given to any other heading apart from a genus.

The term "Arthropods", is the English equivalent for the Phylum Arthropoda (joint-footed creatures) and contains the Classes Insecta, Arachnida, and Crustacea.

Members of the 'Class Insects' have a head, thorax and abdomen, one pair of antennae, three pairs of walking legs, and usually two pairs of wings in the adult.

Members of the 'Class Arachnida' have a fore and hind-body, no antennae, four pairs of walking legs but never wings.

Other queries on this subject may be answered by referring to the subsequent chapters dealing with classification and to the published Rules of Zoological Nomenclature as laid down by International Zoological Congress.

Although this chapter is primarily devoted to the geographical setting of the various groups and species of medical zoology, yet the compulsive reactions of the creatures themselves result in their developing a preference for special habitats, which they find and retain under surprisingly difficult circumstances. A minor example is the preference shown in Saigon by *Xenopsylla cheopis* fleas for dwellings with porous-tile floors, as against the preference shown by the closely related *Xenopsylla astia* for houses with sandy-earthen floors. The difference between the humidity of these two types of floorings clearly demarked the habitats of the two flies species.

The best way of learning practical zoology is by working in the field under the guidance of a local expert or an experienced zoologist or entomologist. Where this is not possible, perhaps a recital of the basic principles governing the geographical distribution of animals of medical importance is the best foundation on which a medical zoologist can build this knowledge for himself.

There are three broad factors affecting the geographical distribution and variation of arthropod species liable to injure human beings:-

1. LATITUDE and ALTITUDE: the visual effect of these two measurements is seen in the changes of plant life, including trees, as a more northerly latitude or a higher altitude is reached, which changes affect the kinds and numbers of arthropods and reptiles found at these levels.

2. TEMPERATURE and HUMIDITY: arthropods being cold-blooded, become most energetic at suitable warm temperatures. As many of them are of delicate structure, e.g. mosquitoes, atmospheric humidity is of great importance to them in resisting dehydration. Also, many arthropod-borne diseases have their optimum incidence in the equatorial zones of 70°F. to 80°F. mean average temperatures, e.g. mosquito-borne malaria; althouh some, such as louse-borne typhus, are associated with colder climatic conditions. Speaking practically the naturalist must always ascertain in advance when the "season", which is usually governed by a combination of temperature and humidity, for any regional or local·outbreaks of arthropod-borne disease or nuisance is to be expected.

3. REGIONAL EVOLUTION and SPECIALISATION: since the Earth is divided by natural barriers, such as oceans and mountains, into regions and subregions, adjacent zones of flora and fauna are often discontinuous, e.g. Asian fauna are markedly different from Australian. This is due to localised evolution having taken place, so that even widely distributed creatures such as flying insects are often restricted to special areas. In this connection it is important to understand that whereas a genus (group of related species) may have a wide geographical range, the individual species which it contains are usually limited by specialisation to types of terrain that suit their requirements, but not those of the other species. An example of this is the genus *Glossina* or tsetse flies, which are found over most of tropical Africa, although each of its species has its own ecological niche, some living only in humid areas, others in dry environments, and so on.

A female mosquito taking a blood meal. Note the "alert" position of the antennae and hind legs and the way in which the outer sheath (labium) of the proboscis is looped back from the inner piercing fascicle.

2

GEOGRAPHICAL DISTRIBUTION OF
INSECTS OF MEDICAL IMPORTANCE

An examination of a map of the world will reveal that the Arctic ice-cap (on ocean) is in close proximity to an almost continuous belt of land, viz: Alaska, Canada, Greenland, Norway, Lapland and Siberia; whereas the Antarctic ice-cap (on rock) is surrounded by permanent ocean (South Pacific, South Atlantic, South Indian Oceans), and is only approached by distant points of the land masses, viz: the tooth-like tip of South America, the pointed land mass of South Africa, and the blunter southernmost tip of Australia. India, the other tooth-like projection of continental land, terminates almost 10° of latitude north of the equator.

The frigid influence of the Arctic ice on the northern coasts of America, Europe and Asia causes the circumpolar belt of land or tundra to remain frozen for some nine to eleven months of the year, an arrangement not paralleled by the Earth's southerly coasts facing the Antarctic.

There is, however, in these northern latitudes a short summer period of one to three months, during which the ground thaws for three feet or less below the surface. This liberates vast quantities of shallow water over thousands of miles of treeless tundra, and causes the eggs of countless mosquitoes to hatch into larvae. These larvae feed voraciously on the underwater debris of dead moss, lichens and Arctic plants, and soon become pupae from which adult mosquitoes emerge. So numerous will these become that they may stretch from horizon to horizon in long clouds.

Men cannot work during the 'around the clock' attacks of these large blood-thirsty female mosquitoes (male mosquitoes are unable to pierce skin and suck blood), unless protected by special clothing including veils, repellents, and chemical insecticidal fogs.

These Arctic mosquitoes belong to the world-wide genus

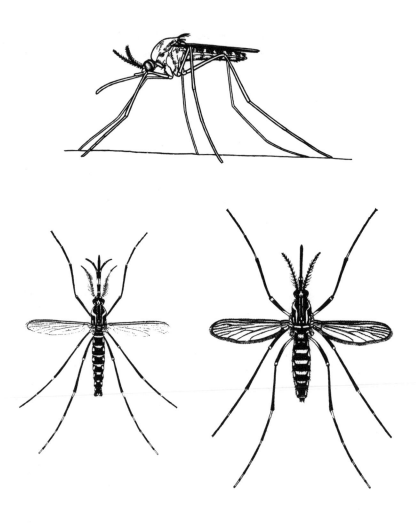

Fig. 1 (Top) the typical resting position of a female culicine mosquito. (Bottom left) male *Aedes aegypti* and (bottom right) female *A. aegypti*. The male has bushy antennae whereas those of the female are sparsely haired.

Aëdes, the females of which specialise in laying eggs unusually resistant to adverse conditions. In this case the eggs withstand nine to eleven months of freezing cold. Other species of *Aëdes* mosquitoes, however, are met with in almost every part of the world, the females typically laying their resistant eggs just above a water line in situations likely to be flooded, e.g. flood plains, ponds, tree-rot holes, broken crocks. The most important species is *Aëdes aegypti* (Fig. 1), a black and white mosquito found only in warm or hot climates, where it will breed rapidly in very small collections of water, such as old tins, coconut-husks, gutters, etc. Its eggs (Fig. 2) are able to resist dry conditions for months, until the stimulus of rising water causes the larvae (Fig. 3) to emerge, when in less than a week the immature forms may develop into adult mosquitoes. *Aëdes aegypti* is the only known vector of the yellow fever virus in urban areas, and it is also a transmitter of the dengue virus, which causes a painful influenza-type fever, throughout its wide range.

Biting mosquitoes, then, of various specialising kinds, are to be expected in any country where there is enough shallow water, fresh or brackish, clean or foul, stagnant or slow moving, in which the aquatic immature stages may find sufficient organic food to develop. The biting female adults may be a simple or serious nuisance, or they may carry disease organisms in their saliva, for example, malaria and yellow fever, or in their proboscis, for instance, certain immature microfilarial worms (e.g. *Wuchereria bancrofti*), according to the habits of their species, and the availability to them of both sick and healthy human hosts. Mosquitoes typically bite outdoors at dusk and dawn, and within-doors throughout the night.

As the treeless tundra becomes more southerly in latitude, scrub-willow and Arctic-birch appear and gradually merge into the zone of Boreal coniferous forest. This deep circumtundral belt of predominantly pine, spruce and larch with some broadleaf or deciduous trees is slightly pushed out of line by the southwards penetration of the large cold water area of Hudson Bay in Canada, but otherwise demonstrates well the influence of latitude on flora and fauna.

This typically cold forest, like the tundra, releases vast quantities of water when the thaw comes, but instead of remaining as surface water, most of the melted snow and ice

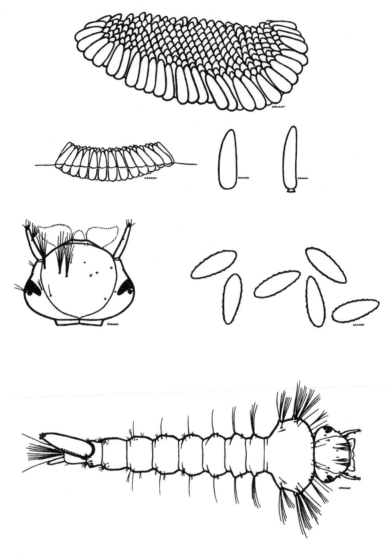

Fig. 2 Eggs of (top) *Culex sp.* in a typical raft formation floating in the water surface; (right centre) *Aedes* sp. laid above the water surface and (bottom) a typical culicine larva with siphon and (left centre) short broad head.

22

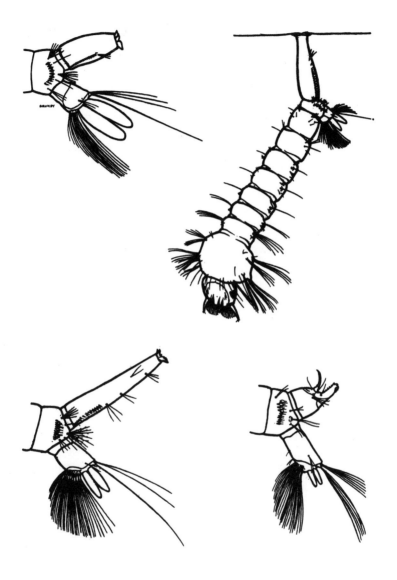

Fig. 3 (Top right) *Culex* larva hanging in typical Culicine position from the water surface, with siphons of *Aedes* (top left), *Culex* (bottom left) and *Mansonia* (bottom right).

forms rapid, often cataract-filled tributaries, joining wide rivers. Since many of these flow from south to north, particularly in Siberia, and tend to flood over the normal lines of communication, they often make it difficult for man to harvest their wealth of softwoods; but at the same time, they form a vast and ideal breeding ground for the little gauzy-winged biting black-fly *Simulium* (Fig. 4), which is the dominant blood-sucker of these forests. In North America their swarms are a serious menace as far south as the Great Lakes.

The females of these flies, which may appear in huge daytime swarms (since blackflies, unlike mosquitoes, do not bite at night), drive the lumberjacks from the rivers, and the hunters from the forests. Their bites frequently give rise to an allergic condition known as "bung-eye", which is a swelling of both eyelids severe enough to prevent the victim being able to see. This has led to a number of deaths caused by shock and exposure. Repellents, antihistamines, protective clothing including veils of mosquito netting, and smoky fires in camp known as 'smudges' are some of the defensive measures open to the naturalist.

Biting black-flies may be found, however, not only in these northern latitudes (including parts of the tundra), but also in any part of the world where there is sufficient well oxygenated water to satisfy the respiratory requirements of the immature forms. This typically means the pools below small waterfalls, which are always saturated with air bubbles, though in parts of tropical Africa, rocks which are constantly wetted by the wave-spray of lakes, and also the backs and legs of semi-aquatic freshwater crabs, may form alternative well-oxygenated habitats for *Simulium* larvae and pupae.

Mass daytime attacks by *Simulium* may occur in other parts of the globe, as for instance, the Danube basin when conditions specially favour their multiplication. They appear to prefer warm cloudy weather and during 'fly years' all animals unable to find shelter are likely to be killed by their multiple bites. These northern and temperate-climate blackfly species, however, do not transmit disease. On the other hand, in tropical Africa (Senegal to the Congo, then east to the Sudan and Kenya), and in some areas of southern Mexico and Guatemala, blackflies transmit *via* their bites the microfilariae which cause

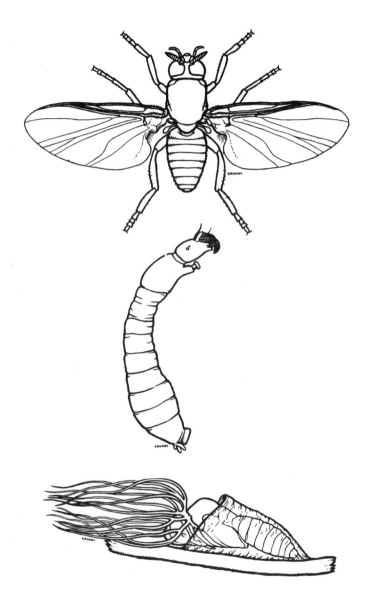

Fig. 4 Adult *Simulium* biting blackfly (top) with larva (centre) and pupa (bottom).

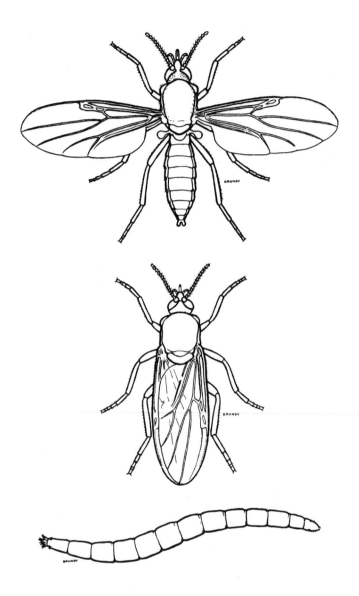

Fig. 5 Adult *Culicoides* biting midge (top and centre) with larva (bottom).

Onchocerciasis to humans living near rivers. This condition results in painful tumours and is associated with blindness among those infected. *Simulium damnosum* is the most important African species.

South of the boreal forest grows the intermixture of coniferous and broadleaf trees, which in theory should deepen into a wide zone of deciduous forest, attuned to a leafy summer for half the year and a leafless winter for the remaining months. In this zone a topsoil of leafmould, loam, or peat should accumulate.

There are two influences, however, which produce zonal discontinuity in these latitudes. The first is man himself, who has burnt or cut down much of the broadleaf forest to make way for farming (Europe, from Scotland to the borders of Spain, and from the Atlantic to the Urals, has largely been so farmed. North America also, from south of the Great Lakes to Florida, and from the Western Prairies to the Atlantic seaboard is undergoing a similar process).

The second influence is the intervention of mountain chains acting as walls running north to south, which adversely affect the passage of moisture-laden clouds from the oceans to the remainder of the 'zone'. The Rocky Mountains of western North America shield central and southern North America; the Ural Mountains divide Europe from Mongolia, and the mountains of Inner Mongolia and Manchuria wall out the Pacific.

The effect of tidy farming is greatly to lessen the dominance of biting arthropods, but there are still large areas belonging to this northern 'soil zone' which are too waterlogged by lack of drainage to be farmed, and it is these acid moors, peaty bogs, fresh or salt-water marsh and vegetative swamps that are the preferred home or focus of tiny biting midges of the genus *Culicoides* (Fig. 5). Although so small, these insects, in the aggressive female form, may appear in such clouds (usually at dusk, but also by day if disturbed) as to render certain areas uninhabitable to man and domestic animals. Parts of Scotland and northern Europe, the seaboard and Everglades of Florida, the West Indies, and Central America are a few geographical examples. The bites of *Culicoides* are sharp and painful and may lead to allergic inflammations and secondary infections. Repellents have a shorter effect than against mosquitoes, and puncture proof clothing is necessary if outdoor work is contemplated where they are numerous. These midges are small enough to creep through mosquito netting and to pass between the head hairs.

The larval forms of the northern species hibernate in the soil during the winter season. There are however, many species which infest other parts of the world, including equatorial marshlands. Some of these tropical African and South American species transmit the microfilariae of certain endoparasitic worms to man, but these are not considered to be pathogenic (as are the *Onchocerca* worms conveyed by *Simulium*).

Although good temperate-region field-agriculture greatly reduces the local mosquitoes, blackflies and midges, because of its efficient drainage of water from the surface to the subsoil, yet farms and houses tend to subsidise other fly pests. The common houseflies, the most important of which is *Musca domestica* (Fig. 6), breed in fermenting vegetable matter such as manure, the lesser housefly *Fannia* (Fig. 7) and the semi-domestic bluebottle, greenbottle and greybottle flies which prefer decomposing animal material and carcasses, are always numerous near human dwellings and garbage heaps.

These flies are not very dangerous in countries which maintain a high standard of hygiene, in spite of their habit of feeding alternatively on faeces and human food, for as long as exposed excreta does not contain dangerous pathogenic organisms such as cholera vibrios, typhoid and dysentery bacilli, dysentery amoebae, polio viruses, etc., nothing worse than the causative organisms of mild diarrhoea or redness of the eyes is likely to be transmitted. In countries where there is a low or nonexistent standard of hygiene and sanitation, and they are in the majority as far as the naturalist is concerned, there is considerable danger of pathogenic viruses, bacteria, protozoa and worm eggs being conveyed mechanically on the mouth parts or body hairs of these 'calypterate' flies to his food or person. It should also be remembered that the non-biting domestic and semi-domestic flies under discussion constantly require access to moisture (which they prefer to obtain from faeces), for they have delicate fleshy lips at the termination of their proboscis or beak, which need to be kept moist from a fluid reservoir or 'crop' in the abdomen. In dry weather therefore, or

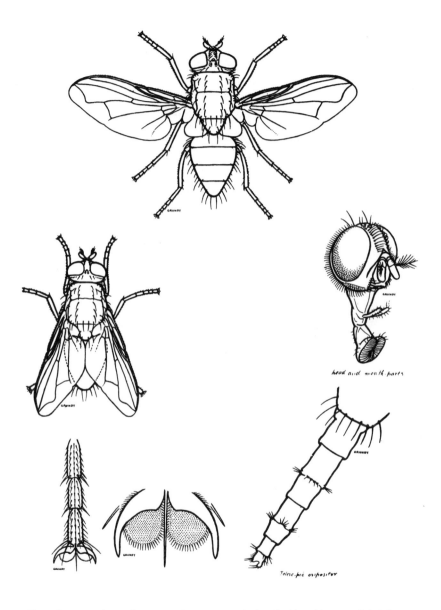

Fig. 6 Common housefly *Musca domestica* with detail of head (centre right), foot and pulvilli (bottom left and centre), and female ovipositor (bottom right).

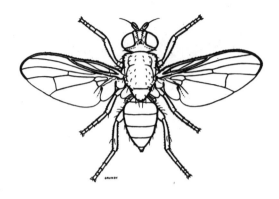

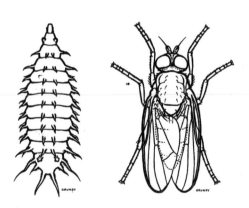

Fig. 7 Lesser housefly *Fannia sp.* with larval stage (bottom left).

in areas of low humidity, human perspiration, eye secretions and lip moisture become desperately attractive to this kind of fly even in the presence of adequate faecal supplies, so that they will endeavour to swarm over the skin unless prevented by clothing, including a veil. Repellents do not have a very lasting effect against the persistence of calypterate flies.

If it is possible, anyone visiting tropical areas close to insanitary human habitations should prepare his own food and do his own cooking, keeping everything edible and potable away from the local fly population.

Generally speaking, the temperate 'soil zone' becomes dryer as the distance from the Atlantic Ocean increases (both as regards North America and Eurasia). East of the Ural Mountains therefore, farming and forest tend to be replaced by treeless coarse grasslands, which may become semi-desert or even desert during periods of prolonged drought. It is always a risk for man to break the living turf by ploughing this type of wild grassland, as such scars take many years to heal if allowed to revert, and easily become dust-bowls.

Such areas of natural grazing are the Steppes of Mongolia, traditionally horse and antelope country, and the Prairies of North America, the natural home of 'buffalo' and 'deer'. They are also the main foci of biting gadflies (Fig. 8), burly often brightly coloured insects ranging from the size of houseflies (woodland type) to that of bumblebees, with a two and a half inches overall wing-span (plains type). These powerfully built gadflies may range for miles away from their marshy breeding grounds in search of host animals, and, by unerring instinct, will eventually fly back to where mud is available by stream or bog in order to lay their eggs. The male, which does not bite or suck blood may also fly far, but only in search of a female.

Unless windborne, mosquitoes, blackflies and midges are typically restricted to half a mile or so from their breeding areas. Houseflies and bluebottles also, though capable of strong flight, prefer to remain near their breeding grounds, but the giant gadflies roam their hunting grounds at will.

Gadflies do not normally convey disease, though in the forest lands of tropical West Africa they are proven vectors of the parasitic worm *Loa loa* and are further suspected over an even wider extension of this continent of mechanically conveying the

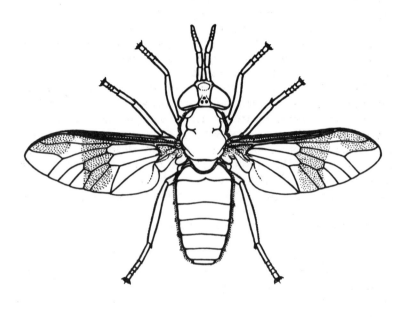

Fig. 8 Adult *Chrysops sp.* gadfly

trypanosomes of sleeping sickness on their mouthparts. The physical attack of their multiple bites however can alone be so severe as to turn the naturalist aside from his project, and to prevent him using horses or mules. In the southern U.S.A. there is one small species of gadfly, known locally as the 'deer fly' (*Chrysops discalis*), which transmits by its bite the bacilli causing tularaemia. It obtains these micro-organisms from the prairie jack-rabbit. An ulcer typically develops at the site of the bite and there may be a severe plague-like fever.

At this point it seems useful to interpose some comments on sylvatic or more correctly 'campestral' or wild-rodent plague, (although this has nothing to do with gadflies), being maintained among wild grassland rodents by fleas. On a number of discontinuous sparsely-inhabited plains of global distribution, the wild rodents are endemically infected with plague bacilli *(Yersinia pestis)* and periodically suffer epizootics of the disease.

The Veld of South Africa (with gerbilles, multimammate mice, etc); the Prairies of North America (with ground squirrels etc.); the Pampas of South America (with cavies etc.); and the Steppes of South Eastern Russia and Mongolia (with susliks, marmots etc.), are examples of sylvatic plague country.

Occasionally an individual human acquires sylvatic plague by negligence or accident (in spite of most species of fleas only changing from their animal-host to man when their preferred host is dead and no others of that species are available). In cold latitudes, this kind of plague tends to become pneumonic in human beings, when the disease ceases to be flea-borne and spreads by droplet infection, and in this way serious epidemics may start. The 'giant marmot' fur-hunters of south-east Russia, and Manchurian soldiers, have died in thousands during epidemics of pneumonic plague.

The precautions, therefore, of avoiding sick animals, of skinning shot or trapped rodents while wearing gloves (to avoid infecting skin abrasions), of cooking thoroughly the bodies of squirrels, marmots etc, when used for food, and of choosing camp sites away from their burrows, are quite important to the field naturalist.

In addition to sylvatic plague (wild-rodent plague) there are sleeping foci of true domestic or commensal rat-borne plague in many rural areas of India, China, Africa, the Middle East etc. As regards these, all that can be said is that the naturalist should take warning if he sees more than a usual number of dead or sick rats, for it is the starving fleas from rats which have died of rat plague that are the transmitting agents to human beings.

In order to image in the mind of the naturalist the terrain in which he is most likely to meet the four ubiquitous outdoor fly pests — mosquitoes, blackflies, midges and gadflies, these insects have carefully been linked with the type of country most suited to their physical requirements.

Gadflies, for instance, have been associated with grazing and grasslands. Their species will, however, like those of the other flies mentioned, also be found wherever conditions enable them to survive, and it is to fit different conditions of climate and environment that the different species have evolved.

Gadflies will be found plaguing the caribou and reindeer of the Canadian and Eurasian tundra. They will be present in the coniferous forest clearings wherever moose, elk or deer provide them with blood-meals, and even on cultivated farm land they can still be a considerable nuisance. They exist also in tropical forests, where, as already mentioned, three species in West Africa, which feed on the blood of tree-top monkeys, are transmitters of the larvae of the parasitic worm *Loa loa*, the adults of which may live in man for fifteen years. Always, wherever they are found, their painful bites are to be avoided by preferably covering the person as much as possible, since repellents are not very effective against these flies.

Mention has been made of the large bluebottle-type flies which are associated with man (Fig. 9), typically under farming conditions. The bluebottle, greenbottle and greybottle flies are essentially scavengers and will quickly find and 'blow' with their eggs or first stage larvae any animal which has died. Some species however, do not wait for the death of the 'host', but lay their eggs or deposit first stage maggots on the living body, typically in the vicinity of the smallest scratch or bruise. These are the 'myiasis' flies. They cause considerable mortality among flocks and herds if the wounds made by their larvae are not treated in time, and there are numerous cases of deaths in humans, particularly after the nasal and ear passages have been 'struck' with the eggs or larvae. A discharging sore exposed

34

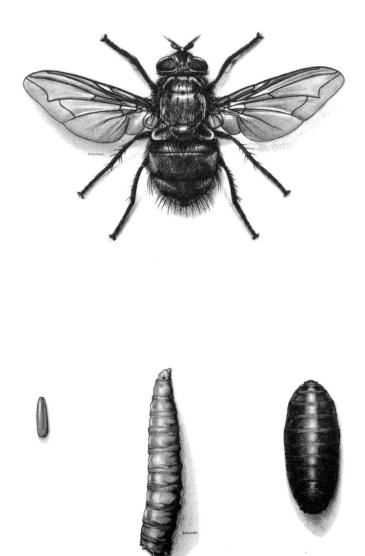

Fig. 9 Bluebottle, *Calliphora sp.* with adult (top), egg (left), larva (centre) and puparium (right). (Many flies pupate in the skin of the mature larva. This stage is known as a puparium rather than a pupa).

during a period of daytime sleep is attractive to the gravid females, and the sight of an eye may be lost through the penetration of a single larva (greybottle flies may larviposit one to four larvae at a single 'strike' or 'lay').

Although largely concentrating on the flocks and herds of grasslands, myiasis flies may be found in most warm and hot countries and some are well known by name. The primary screw-worm fly of south western North America (= New World screw-worm fly *Callitroga americana*), is notorious for its attacks on animals and man, and so is the Old World screw-worm fly *(Chrysomyia bezziana)*, which mainly infests humans in India and animals in Africa.

In tropical South America the 'Human Bot-fly' *(Dermatobia hominis)* which does not feed at all, unlike the semi-domestic 'calypterate' flies lays its eggs on the underside of a biting calypterate fly *Stomoxys*, or on a jungle mosquito, especially selecting members of the genus *Psorophora*. When these insects bite a human host, one or more of the eggs attached to them will hatch, and the resulting maggots quickly bore into the surface tissues. Severe ulceration and secondary infections often result, since the larvae may remain *in situ* for several months.

Widely distributed throughout tropical Africa is the infamous Tumbu fly *(Cordylobia anthropophaga)* (Fig. 10) which lays its eggs on ground retaining a human smell (latrines or camping sites). The maggots which hatch from these eggs climb on any stationary host and quickly burrow just below the skin. Eruptions follow which are usually mistaken for painful boils. Newly washed shirts, vests, or pants should not be laid out to dry on ground suspected of being within the range of these yellow coloured bluebottle-like flies.

One might expect that as the climatic temperature increased southwards of the 'soil' belt ("deciduous forest" and "steppe") there might develop a parallel belt of semi-desert and desert. This to some extent occurs, as south and east of the Steppes the Gobi desert is found (landlocked between the Mongolian mountains and the Pacific ocean coastal ranges). The zone of desert that continues westwards of the Gobi however, does not follow the lines of latitude as it approaches the Mediterranean, but after a last stand around the Aral Sea, tilts downwards to absorb north-west India, Iran, Arabia and

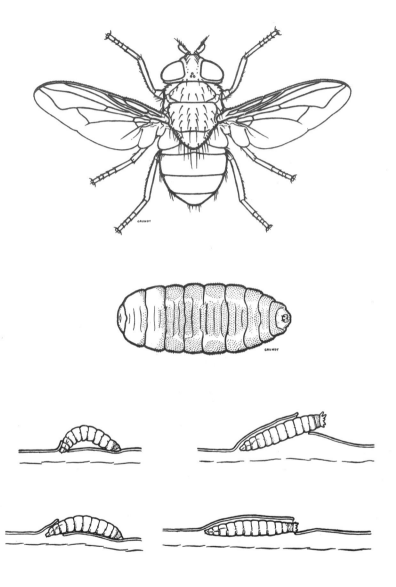

Fig. 10 Tumbu fly *Cordylobia anthropophaga* with larva (centre). Lower drawings show the way in which the larva burrows into living tissue, causing specific myiasis.

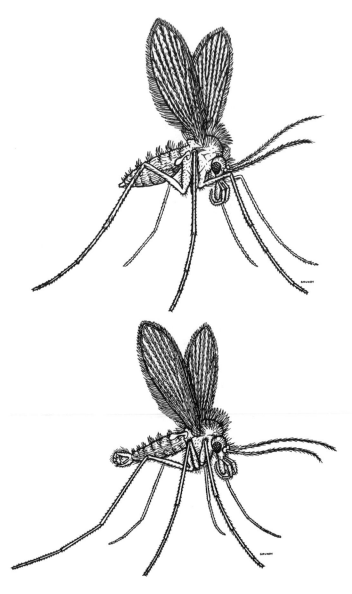

Fig. 11 Sandfly *Phlebotomus sp.*, adult female (top) and male with prominent genital claspers (bottom).

approximately the northern third of the African continent, leaving, however, most of the lands surrounding the Mediterranean Sea as a region with a climate of its own (including Morocco, Algeria, Tunisia and the Nile Valley and Delta).

If the western bulge of the African continent can be imagined as fitting into the Caribbean Sea, as in the theory of Continental Drift, then one would note that this looping belt of desert continues in to south west U.S.A., northern Mexico and northwards into the Rocky Mountains. These deserts of the northern hemisphere are approximately north and south of the Tropic of Cancer. There are also balancing desert areas centered on the Tropic of Capricorn, namely, the Chilean, Patagonian, South-west African, Kalahari, and great Australian deserts.

Since desert is land where flora and fauna find it difficult to survive, a naturalist in such regions (which occupy about one fifth of the Earth's surface) would not expect to be attacked by many insects. Travel in deserts, however, is always from one water supply to another, so he must expect to be bitten by mosquitoes at such oases or camp sites as are associated with water. The Sahara desert in particular will be found to contain species of *Anopheles* mosquito that specialise in breeding in the brackish water which is typical of deserts, and these mosquitoes are usually vectors of malaria, for many of the human inhabitants of the region are reservoirs of the disease. Malaria drug prophylaxis, and/or repellents and mosquito nets are therefore necessary in parts of this otherwise barren terrain. *Anopheles sergenti* and *Anopheles multicolor* are probably the most important African desert species.

Returning to the Mediterranean Region, which has a warm but not tropical climate throughout most of the year (although the southern parts are considerably hotter than the northern European coasts) we find that this environment suits the very small sandfly or *Phlebotomus* (Fig. 11), which demands a microclimate in warm damp fissures for its immature stages, together with sufficient organic debris in the breeding sites for the larvae to feed on. Though common in the Mediterranean region, different species of sandflies are found to occupy most coastal and mountainous areas of the world, wherever they are able to find the above conditions (habitats) for breeding. They therefore live in a circumglobal zone of their own which is not easily recognised by its appearance, avoiding only cold northern climates and uncongenial altitudes. They are even more of a biting nuisance than midges, where they are numerous, and come out to feed as the sun goes down, continuing throughout the night until satiated with blood. They easily penetrate mosquito netting when hungry but cannot escape when engorged. Repellents are of some help, and an overhead fan, where such a luxury is available, will blow sandflies aside, as they are weak fliers.

Sandflies may roughly be divided into those living in dryish areas and those preferring wet or monsoon conditions. Species of dry area sandflies transmit the viruses of sandfly fever in many parts of their range, and whereas the local inhabitants may be immune to this short influenzal-type fever, non-immune visitors may go down with the illness shortly after entering a sandfly district. Sandfly bites are difficult to avoid at night, (though long sleeves and trousers assist in the evening), because sandfly netting is of such small mesh that anyone trying to sleep under it has difficulty in breathing during hot weather. The other and more serious disease transmitted by dry-area sandflies, such as *Phlebotomus papatasii* and *Phlebotomus sergenti,* is cutaneous leishmaniasis or oriental sore (Fig. 12), which in the Mediterranean region is usually acquired from the bite of a sandfly which has been feeding from the edge of a sore on a dog. North Africa, the Middle East, northern India, Indo-China and Queensland in Australia are the principle foci.

The wet-area sandflies are incriminated in the transmission of the serious disease visceral leishmaniasis, often referred to as kala azar. The disease tends to break out after the rains, when sandflies such as *Phlebotomus argentipes* seasonally flourish. Bengal, Burma and Assam, Eastern China, and the Mediterranean coastline including Sicily, are the principal foci, with some cases reported from the Argentine.

In Central and South America the muco-cutaneous form of leishmaniasis is endemic. It is transmitted by local sandflies mainly in the humid forest regions below 2,000 ft. and the chicle-gum tappers suffer severely from this dreadfully disfiguring disease.

There is also a very limited but none the less important illness

Fig. 12 The cycle of the *Leishmania* parasite in the sandfly *Phlebotomus*. The organism is taken up in a blood meal from an infected host (top), develops within the sandfly (centre), and is passed on to a new host in a subsequent blood meal (bottom).

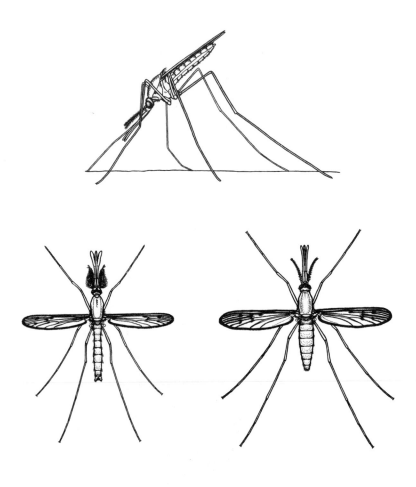

Fig. 13 Female *Anopheles* mosquito showing the typical Anopheline resting position (top) (compare this with the Culicine in Fig. 1), and adult male (lower left) and female (lower right).

called oroya fever. This sandfly-transmitted disease is found only in certain valleys on the western slopes of the Andes in South America between 1,000 ft. and 12,000 ft. Non-immune visitors are almost certain to acquire the disease if they enter the valleys just after the rainy season, and unfortunately the course of the illness is usually very rapid, with a profound anaemia that frequently terminates in death within three weeks.

Sandflies, as has been said, have a circumglobal distribution around the warmer parts of the world wherever suitably warm and humid microclimates can be found in rocks, rubble or soil. A somewhat similar circumglobal distribution of much greater importance is that of the malaria mosquitoes (genus *Anopheles*) (Figs. 13, 14 & 15). These slender blood-sucking gnats typically transmit various forms of this disease trom the deciduous-tree farming-belt southwards to the Tropic of Capricorn (which approximately divides South America in half, runs through the southern tip of Madagascar and the northern forest regions of Australia).

Temperature seems to be the limiting factor, for the malaria parasites in the mosquito tend to lose their viability below 60°F., and reach maximum efficiency in the zone of 80°F. or more, always provided that the atmospheric humidity is sufficient to assure longevity in the mosquito vectors.

It is essential therefore, that apart from using repellents and mosquito nets, field workers in the tropics and subtropics adhere to chemical malarial prophylaxis unless they are visiting some of the few non-malarious areas of the world such as the Hawaiian Islands. Also, the presence of a large healthy-looking native population does not necessarily mean there is no endemic malaria awaiting the new-comer, for many native races acquire a degree of immunity.

The remaining kind of terrain which is clearly separated from the zones so far described, is the opposite of the desert. It is the evergreen tropical rain-forest. In these hot, humid areas, the forests of tall straight-trunked hardwoods tower into the sky, with their upper branches and leaves forming a continuous 'canopy' that tends to blot out the sunlight from the ground below.

There is no global zone of rain-forest, but if the continents were again imagined to be closed up as in the theory of

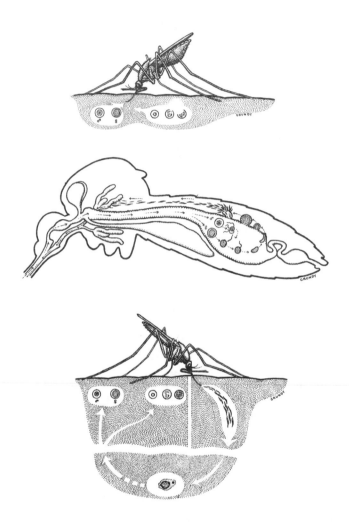

Fig. 14 The cycle of the *Plasmodium* parasite in the *Anopheles* mosquito. The female mosquito takes up the malarial parasite from an infected human during a bloodmeal (top), the parasite develops and multiplies in the mosquito (centre) and is passed to an uninfected human in the mosquito's saliva in a subsequent bloodmeal (bottom).

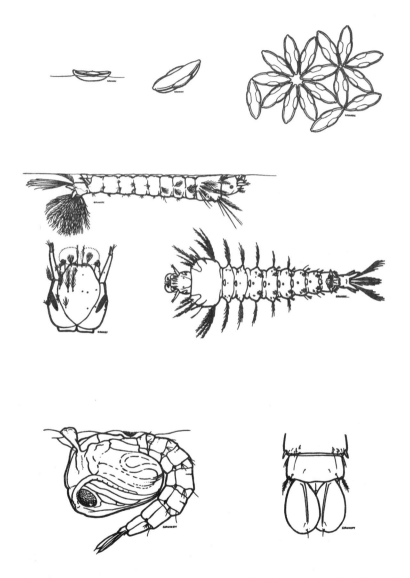

Fig. 15 Eggs of an Anopheline mosquito (top) typically boat-shaped with lateral air-floats; larval stage (centre) with no siphon; typical mosquito pupa (bottom) with posterior paddles. The pupal stage of both Anopheline and Culicine mosquitoes is very similar.

Continental Drift, then one could see that the vast rain-forests of the Amazon basin in South America would be continuous with the rain-forests of West Africa (Ivory Coast, Ghana, Nigeria) and the Congo basin, and that these in turn would connect with the tropical forests of Burma, Indo-China, Malaya, Indonesia, the Philippines, and northern Australia.

Apart from the ubiquitous malaria mosquito, which flourishes over most of these territories, the rain-forest zone must be divided into separate regions for purposes of understanding the distribution of insect vectors of disease.

Mention has already been made of the three species of *Chrysops* gadflies, which normally inhabit the sunlit forest canopy of west and central Africa including the Congo basin.

Of greater medical interest is the fact that the two largest rain-forests in the world, namely, the Amazon basin and Congo basin areas, are the endemic reservoirs of the yellow fever virus. Although it was believed in 1925 that yellow fever had been completely eradicated, it has since been found that the disease is maintained among the tree-top monkeys by 'canopy' mosquitoes, and this endemic form of the disease is known as 'jungle' yellow fever. Occasionally humans are bitten by infected jungle mosquitoes and develop the disease. If they are transported back to an area where *Aedes aegypti,* the 'urban' yellow fever vector abounds (and that is in most tropical inhabited places) then there is a possibility that a local epidemic of yellow fever may begin.

It is one of the mysteries of medicine, however, that there has never been any yellow fever outside America and Africa (and at one time Western Europe), although the urban mosquito vector is extremely common throughout India, Indo-China, the 'East India Islands' and Australia.

In discussing the African rain-forest, trypanosomiasis or African sleeping-sickness must be included. Its relationship with tsetse flies (Figs. 16, 17 & 18) also gives an opportunity to explain how an insect genus may have a focus of terrain in which it prefers to live, without by any means confining it to that region, so long as it can adapt its species to other accessible areas. For instance, the most important tsetse fly in tropical Africa is *Glossina palpalis.* This is a 'wet-riverine species' not found away from the cover of leafy trees associated with rivers, lakes and

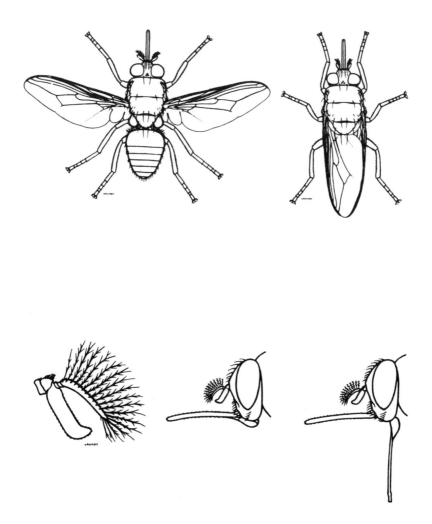

Fig. 16 Adult tsetse fly *Glossina sp.* (top) with detail of antenna (bottom left), and head and mouth parts, the proboscis in the feeding position at bottom right.

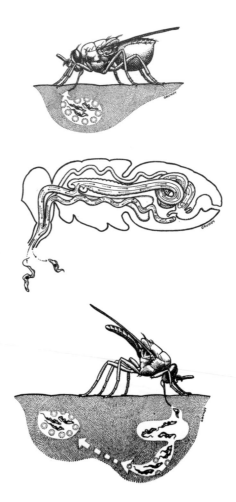

Fig. 17 Cycle of the African sleeping sickness *Trypanosoma* in the tsetse fly. Both male and female fly may take up the parasite from an infected man or animal during a bloodmeal (top); the organism undergoes development in the fly (centre), and is passed on to a new host in a subsequent bloodmeal (bottom).

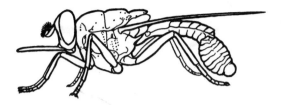

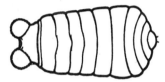

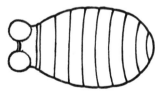

Fig. 18 Adult female tsetse (top) with developing larva in abdomen, mature third stage larva (centre) and puparium (bottom).

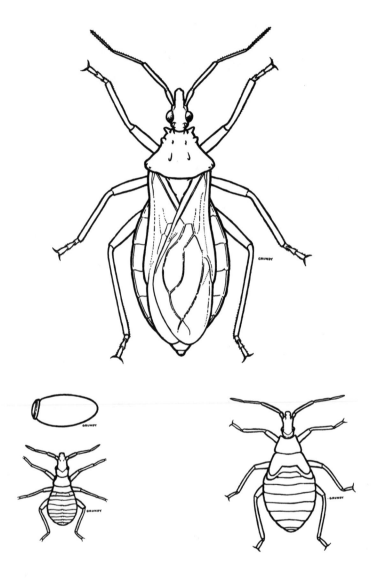

Fig. 19 Cone-nose bug (subfamily Triatominae) adult (top), with egg and two of the five nymphal (immature) stages (bottom).

streams. Professor Buxton once told me that as he flew across West Africa, he could see far below the green lines of trees edging the rivers; "those lines are the home of *palpalis*" he said. Other tsetse-fly species, however, are not limited by this particular floral boundary; for instance, a smaller variety has evolved which is able to extend its range almost to the Sahara desert, where in the dry season the rivers contract into pools surrounded by a few palms. This tsetse is the 'dry-riverine species' *Glossina tachinoides*. Again, eastwards and southwards of Lake Victoria are the 'steppes' of East Africa, the chosen areas of the game herds of gnu and zebra. Here in the grass and scrub savannah lives another specialisation, the species *Glossina swynnertoni*, which in the hot season lives on its animal hosts almost like a tick, running to keep in the shade and only flying directly from one animal to another. As there are twenty-three species of tsetse in all, it can be realised how well this genus of tropical African flies has explored all avenues of survival. Apart from avoiding "fly belts", well known to the natives, there is not much the field naturalist can do to discourage the painful attentions of these day-biting flies.

Leaving aside zonal terrains at this point, mention must be made of the trypanosomiasis found in tropical America, which is a different illness to that found in tropical Africa. The micro organisms of this American disease are found in the alimentary tract of 'cone-nose bugs' over a vast area from the southern U.S.A. to mid-Argentina, but human cases have so far been limited to scattered villages ranging from southern Mexico to Uruguay. The vectors are blood-sucking bugs (subfamily Triatominae) (Fig. 19) which though represented by similar species in many other countries, convey the trypanosomes only in America. Transmission occurs while the bugs are feeding, typically on the face of a human wrapped in a blanket and asleep in a hammock, and strangely enough, not by way of the insect's saliva but in its faecal discharge, which is evacuated on the host's skin during the blood-meal. The trypanosomes are later rubbed into the bite-puncture, the eyes, the corners of the mouth, or shaving abrasions, usually by the host when he awakes. Avoidance of the floor of adobe huts when resting, and the use of a mosquito-net well tucked in the hammock, are the best ways of diverting the attentions of these unpleasant flying bugs. Usually the bites of cone-nose bugs are not painful, hence the term 'kissing bugs', but some species, such as *Triatoma protracta*, may cause by their bites symptoms of pain, palpitation and urticaria similar to those caused by the stings of bees and wasps in susceptible persons.

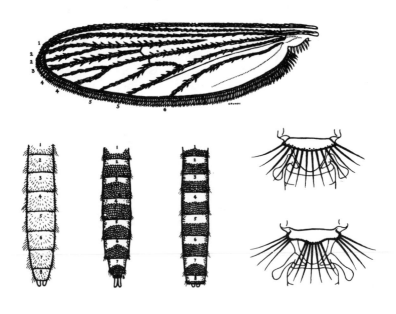

Typical wing venation of a mosquito (top) with abdomens of female *Anopheles* (bottom left), *Aedes* (centre) and *Culex* (right centre), and scutellums of adult Anopheline (right above) and Culicine (right below).

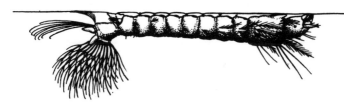

Larva of Anopheline (top) and Culicine (bottom) mosquito. Whereas the Culicine larva, has its spiracles on the end of a siphon and hangs vertically from the water surface when obtaining atmospheric oxygen, the Anopheline has no siphon and lies parallel to the water surface.

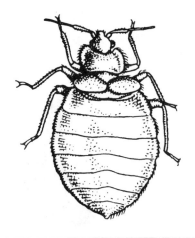

Bedbug *Cimex lectularius.*

3

INSECT PARASITES PERSONAL TO MAN

The student of entomology will be aware that not all insect pests prefer a geographical terrain as their chosen habitat. There are some which are parasites of man himself, and therefore are found wherever he goes, for he is their habitat.

The Human louse *(Pediculus humanus)*(Fig. 20), lives only on the blood of man *(Homo sapiens)*, and will die when taken away from him. The Eskimo in the far north, and the Singhalese near the equator may equally well harbour this parasite. There are two varieties, head-lice found on the head-hairs, and body-lice, which are larger than head-lice and spend most of their life in the clothing of man. Where no clothes are worn typically only head-lice are found. These two kinds of lice, when they feed on a sick human with typhus rickettsiae in his blood, are unable to prevent the organisms multiplying in the cells lining their own mid-gut, so that their faeces will be mixed, not only with enormous numbers of typhus rickettsiae but with the broken down debris of the stomach cells which the micro-organisms have destroyed. Because of this, the louse will die of the infection within a fortnight, but it may well have infected one or more humans during that period. Man invariably infects himself, either by scratching the rickettsiae into the skin (the more frequent route), or by breathing contaminated dust (physicians and nurses usually become infected in this way). Typhus epidemics have typically been associated with crowded conditions (usually in winter time), when the lice are able easily to wander from person to person, and are more common in temperate than in tropical climates (where fewer clothes are worn to harbour body-lice). Crowded rest-houses or ships, beseiged towns, and refugees huddling together in cold weather are typical examples of typhus 'terrain'. The countries in which the naturalist is most likely to meet louse-borne typhus are those temperate regions where there is a low standard of hygiene and fastidiousness.

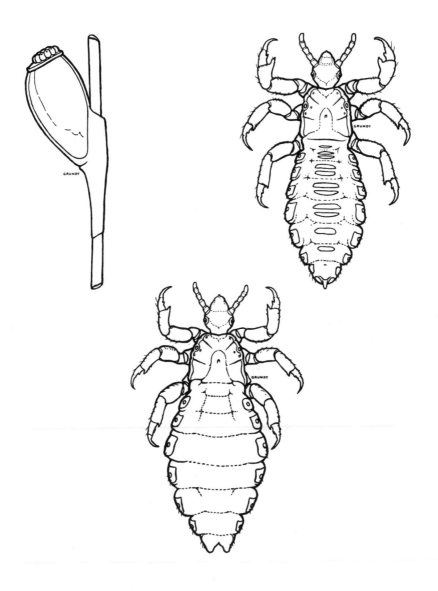

Fig. 20 Egg ("nit") of the human head louse *Pediculus humanus capitis* stuck to a hair (top left), with adult male human louse (top right) and female (bottom).

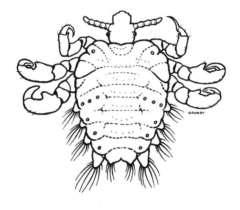

Fig. 21 Crab or pubic louse *Phthirus pubis.*

The second disease conveyed by human lice is relapsing fever, which, like louse-borne typhus, has a high death rate. This tends to occur most frequently in warm climates though there have been epidemics as far north as Ireland. The disease can only be acquired if the human host bites the louse between the teeth, or cracks it between the thumb-nails, or in some cases when the louse is crushed during scratching, for neither the saliva nor the faeces are normally infective, the spirochaetes of relapsing fever being in the blood of the louse, and therefore need to be liberated on to a thin part of the skin before they can enter the human host. Fortunately there is a simple preventative for all to use. A dusting of insecticide will rid the person of lice in a few hours, and this, in conjunction with reasonable cleanliness, should protect anyone against two of man's most ancient pestilences. The third human louse, the squat sedentary pubic louse or 'crab'-louse *(Phthirus pubis)* (Fig. 21), is another specific parasite of the human species. It causes considerable itching and occasionally travels up the chest-hairs and beard to infest the eyelids where it is very difficult to extract from the hair follicles. These pubic-lice, fortunately, carry no known disease.

Human beings also have their own flea species, *Pulex irritans,* which, though occasionally found on other mammals, is the one most usually found on man. It may cause loss of sleep as it runs about the body beneath the clothes, and the allergic response to its frequent bites may lead to scratching and secondary infection. The reason many fleas bite so strongly and continuously is that they tend to indulge in orgasms of feeding, during which they squirt blood in excess of their requirements through their anus. Flea-infested dogs and cats may be recognised by the rough feel of their fur, which will typically be spattered with little specks of dried blood acquired in this manner.

Human fleas may transmit plague bacilli under special conditions, but the plague flea *par excellence* is *Xenopsylla cheopis* (Fig. 22), one of the tropical rat fleas, which has a very wide distribution in warm countries. Because the valve at the entrance to its mid-gut 'blocks' more readily with growing colonies of plague bacilli than in any other flea, this species becomes very thirsty once it is infective, and will bite one host after another in an attempt to obtain blood, inoculating the

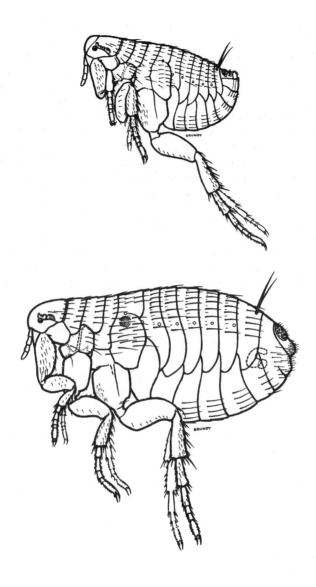

Fig. 22 Tropical rat flea *Xenopsylla cheopis*, male (top) and female (bottom).

causal organisms of bubonic plague as it proceeds.

Once again, therefore, it is advised that should naturalists observe rodents dying of disease, they should immediately take precautions against plague (on the person insecticide powder is very effective against fleas). If one of these creatures is captured between the thumb and forefinger, do not try merely to squeeze it to death, for being normally flattened from side to side, this pressure is not very effective against fleas. Instead, rub the finger and thumb against each other; this destroys the flea's capacity to jump free, by disjointing its legs from the body. A wet tablet of soap is a very effective chaser of the odd flea or bed-bug, as they adhere to its soft surface the moment it touches them.

There are occasions, however, when the explorer may meet more than the odd flea. For instance, he may enter a building which has been unoccupied for some time and suddenly find an army of fleas crawling up his legs. These are unfed fleas which have been waiting within their pupal cocoons in crevices of the floor, and have emerged only in response to the foot vibrations of a potential host (there is a record of a 1,108 days waiting period). Since these fleas are starving, it is recommended that the human intruder retreats as soon as possible, unless he is one of those rare people who are impervious to the bites of those creatures.

A flea of considerable importance in parts of tropical America and tropical Africa (including Madagascar) is the jigger flea *(Tunga penetrans)* (Fig. 23). It is here included among the personal parasites of man because it lacks a recognisable 'terrain'. This flea seems to prefer uniformly hot dry conditions with some shade in which to live, in contrast to most other fleas, which generally require a high humidity (or rather a carefully balanced temperature and humidity), either in the nest or burrow of their host or on its body. Jigger fleas are usually picked up by man when he is walking along hot dusty roads soiled with the excreta of domestic animals (the flea larvae feed on this organic matter). Unfed male and female jiggers are the smallest of the fleas liable to attack humans, but when the mated female has attached herself and finally burrowed into the skin tissues (the classical place is below the big toe-nail, though the sites may be in any part of the body), she soon grows into the largest flea known to infest man. This is because, when *in situ*, her abdomen

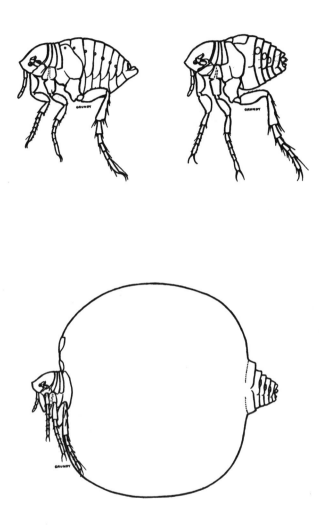

Fig. 23 Jigger flea *Tunga penetrans*, male (top left) and female (top right), with gravid female (bottom).

Fig. 24 The bed bug *Cimex lectularius* adult (top) with egg and two of the five immature (nymphal) stages.

gradually swells with an egg mass until it becomes the size of a small pea, which is a comparatively large and painful foreign body to maintain, particularly in a tropical climate. There may be upwards of thirty such lesions on one person, and many human deaths have occurred through secondary infections following in the wake of such infestations. Sepsis usually occurs as the result of crude efforts to dissect out the egg-filled female jigger, so that home surgery should always be carried out as antiseptically as possible. The local inhabitants are often adept at winkling out these gravid females, but it is best to prevent jigger infection by wearing high boots with sealed tongues, and to place insect repellent around the trousers where they are tucked into the boots.

Another personal parasite of man is the common flightless bed-bug, *Cimex lectularius* (Fig. 24). This blood-sucking insect, together with its twin species *Cimex hemipterus*, is found all over the world in the habitations of man, wherever these properties are not too cold for it to survive the winter months. It has the strange but effective habit of living in cracks and crevices during the day, and of coming forth at night to suck blood from the nearest sleeping host. While not transmitting any disease, its bites can give rise to inconvenient inflammations liable to secondary infections if scratched, and sometimes, in persons sensitive to bugs, bitten eyelids may become so swollen as to prevent the host being able to see on awaking in the morning. These bugs lack one advantage possessed by their tropical American cousins the cone-nose bugs, for they are unable to fly through windows to find their hosts. To make up for this absence of wings they are expert wall climbers, and will cross ceilings in order to drop accurately upon sleepers, on those occasions when the precaution of standing the bed-legs in tins of paraffin has been adopted. A residual spray of insecticide is very effective in killing bed-bugs which have made their home in huts or buildings which it is necessary to occupy.

Among the many calypterate flies that share man's habitat, perhaps the most domestic is the Congo floor-maggot fly of tropical Africa (Fig. 25). This is a 'yellow-bottle' somewhat similar in appearance to the tumbu fly which inhabits much the same regions. The adult floor-maggot flies haunt the shadows of native dwellings and rarely fly outside the compound. The

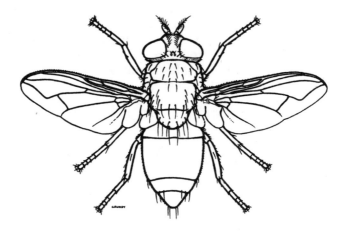

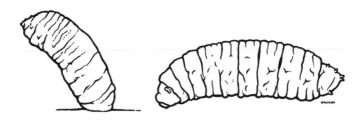

Fig. 25 Congo floor maggot fly *Auchmeromyia luteola* adult (top) with larval stage sucking blood (bottom left) and resting (bottom right).

female seeks deep shade inside a hut in order to lay her eggs on the earth floor, and her maggots, when they hatch, adopt the habits of bed-bugs, by feeding at night on the blood of persons sleeping on the floor. When replete they retire to crevices or burrow in the dust, and eventually pupate. When man changes his ancient habit of sleeping on the ground to sleeping in a bed on raised legs, then the maggots lose their food supply and die out.

The last insect to be placed in the list of 'insects personal to man' is the often referred to *Aedes aegypti* (refer to figures 1 to 3). This is the most domestic of tropical mosquitoes and finds the habitations of man not only suitable breeding sites (the larvae and pupae will develop rapidly in pitchers of drinking water or in flower vases), but man himself a preferred host for blood meals. The adult females will bite by day as well as night, and approach very gently with little whining of wings, and attack such unprotected parts as the ankles and back of the neck. These mosquitoes are, as has been stated, the vectors of urban yellow fever (now rare, thanks to unremitting medical vigilance and anti-yellow fever measures), and dengue fever, (which is still a common and widespread illness). They also transmit the immature forms of the filarial worms that cause elephantiasis in man, but fortunately most Europeans do not seem to stay long enough in filariasis areas to acquire this disfiguring disease.

There are of course, many other semi-domestic insects (including several mosquito species) which appreciate the shelter of man's habitations and the taste of his blood. The most important, however, have already been associated with certain geographical areas.

4

GEOGRAPHICAL DISTRIBUTION OF VENOMOUS INSECTS

The tropical rain-forests occur in those regions where maximum temperature and humidity are combined. In order of size, these forests occupy the following areas — the Amazon basin, with parts of Central America; the Congo basin, extending to the West African coast, and also eastern Madagascar; the IndoChina mainland (western coastal India, north-eastern India southwards through Burma etc. and the 'Islands' to New Guinea); and northern and eastern coastal Australia. These areas are also the most suitable for the development and metabolism of terrestrial (including aerial)arthropods and so it is in this environment that the largest and most aggressive forms occur.

One order of insects, the Hymenoptera, which includes the ants, bees, wasps and hornets, is strongly represented in these optimum regions, and is the more unavoidable because most have evolved as social insects with strong defensive instincts, which means that if one of a colony is disturbed or harmed, then the whole nest or hive may come to the aid of the individual.

The tail-segments in primitive forms of Hymenoptera are typically modified to form a piercing egg-laying tube or ovipositor, at first intended to penetrate crevices and rotted wood (as in saw-flies), and in later forms to paralyse, and to inject eggs into the bodies of other arthropods (as in ichneumons). In those Hymenoptera likely to attack the naturalist, the final stage of ovipositor-evolution has been reached, when this tool has become specialised to form a puncturing and stinging weapon, complete with poison apparatus.

Although found at their largest and fiercest in hot humid forest-lands, less active but none the less dangerous species of Hymenoptera occur in more temperature zones. These typically pass the cold season of the year at some stage by hibernating in a chosen microclimate underground or in hollow trees or among rocks. Temperate region hive-bees, wasps and hornets all give painful stings, the effects of which on humans may vary from local irritation in immune individuals, to profound systemic symptoms, possibly ending in death, in susceptible persons. The presence of histamine may account for the local skin reactions, but the poisoning agent is apparently a foreign protein of low molecular weight. The toxic effects are often augmented by shock leading to collapse. Neutralizing substances are of little use, applied surgical spirit being perhaps as good as any, for not only is it a solvent of the poison, but it cools the skin by evaporation and prevents the entry of secondary infections.

Other less well known examples of stinging Hymenoptera in non-tropical areas are the "velvet ants" (small black pubescent wingless female wasps with a scarlet band), which sting bathers around Lake Erie in North America; and the "Fire-ants", recent invaders of the southern United States of America, which deliver a fiery sting, the wound from which is slow to heal. Since there is some confusion regarding the "biting" and "stinging" of ants, the method employed by the fire-ant may explain the difference. The angry fire-ant bites its victim's skin surface together with its mandibles, and then inserts the tail-sting for about twenty seconds, after which this may be withdrawn and reinserted nearby. Resultant sterile pustules are typical. Multiple stings may cause severe allergic generalised reactions ending in death.

Both the "velvet ants" and "fire-ants" of North America have relatives in the tropical forest regions of South America, which are larger in size and more dangerous to humans. Some ant species are able to spray formic acid from their mouth parts at an enemy, while others inject this as a toxic substance into the bite puncture made by their mandibles.

Accounts by explorers in tropical forests describe many species of both ants and wasps which are locally dreaded by the natives, and are given names that often have no scientific equivalent. Some, however, are particularly notorious, and a few will be referred to, but they do not represent the great number of venomous insects that may actually be encountered, particularly in tropical South America. There is the carnivorous "tucandera", *Paraponera clavata*, of tropical Central and South America. This, like most of the comparatively primitive ponerine ants, nests in small colonies in the ground. They may easily be disturbed, and since they frequently climb into bushes, they may attack explorers on jungle paths. The pain caused by their stings (not 'bites', in spite of their mandibles being large and powerful) is said to be "indescribable", and there is always the danger to an individual of becoming so paralized that he cannot reach his camp. Another member of the ponerine ants is the 'bull-dog" ant of Australia (Myrmicia), which grows to over two centimetres, and bites and stings with such ferocity that few observations of it have been made in the wild state!

The dreaded Driver ants of tropical regions are doryline ants with carnivorous habits. They are blind, but able to communicate with each other as their vast armies, often hundreds of yards long, forage for insects, snakes, or any other living thing which cannot outdistance them. They are most active in overcast weather and at night, and their sorties are timed to the larval requirements, for, although they do not live in underground nests, they bring up their young in large semibivouacs.

It is obviously impossible to cover the subject of stinging and biting ants in the space available, although the subject is an important one for the field naturalist, especially as there are several species in the tropics which cause blindness by attacking the eyelids or the cornea at night. It is suggested, therefore, as a general precaution that all vegetation around a jungle camp should be removed as completely as possible (preferably by burning), and that all food should be carefully sealed in tins or bags, so that ants are not tempted to "rob" the camp (many other Hymenoptera are also keen "robbers") because, once this begins it develops into a compulsive habit and causes endless difficulties leading to many bites and stings.

Even inside permanent buildings many species of ants are capable of seriously hindering scientific work. Some forage in strength for the smallest particles of food (especially sugar), and may attack sleeping persons (e.g. Monomorus). It is ants of this type which attack the eyelids of sleepers in upper Egypt. It is wise,. then, whenever the explorer has a bed, to stand the legs in tins of insect repellent, the most usually available being kerosene.

It should be noted that worker and soldier ants, which are the castes responsible for defence and attack, are always wingless. Bees and wasps on the other hand, mostly have the power of flight added to the ability to sting. This may be serious if the nest is accidently blundered into, or if the naturalist arrives after some animal such as a honey-eating bear has upset the stingers. There are numerous records of deaths caused by swarms of wasps or hornets attacking humans in force, the tropical species in particular being very fierce and easily stirred to wrath. The large Indian hornet *(Vespa magnifica)* is well known for its habit of following those who have angered it, and for its determination to sting, when it has caught up with the object of its annoyance.

It is this tendency of persistent vindicitiveness in the winged Hymenoptera that makes them especially dangerous, and when size, flight, activity, and toxic-sting are united not merely in one fearless individual but in an army of individuals, then retreat into a dark shelter, such as the interior of a building, or into water deep enough to provide cover, is the only alternative to serious consequences.

NOTE: it should not be forgotten that termites, which are erroneously called "white ants", will destroy clothes in trunks left on the floor in infested buildings, and will also eat away the insides of books and reports, leaving only the outer edges and covers, for these creatures cannot tolerate daylight.

5

SCORPIONS AND CENTIPEDES
OF MEDICAL IMPORTANCE

The fundamental difference between the Arachnids (scorpions, spiders, ticks, mites etc.) and the Insects (bugs, flies, etc.) is that arachnids show no tendency to an aerial life, whereas the majority of adult insects are associated with the power of flight. Chilopods (centipedes) though closer to insects than the arachnids (centipedes have an insectan-type head with one pair of antennae) also show no tendency to develop wings. Spiders alone show agility in leaving the ground by leaping, pouncing, and hanging by a thread, whereas all scorpions, ticks, mites and centipedes are crawlers or belly-walkers.

Therefore, the medical entomologist will find the arachnids and chilopods he most wishes to avoid or to collect or to observe, either on the ground itself or lurking in piles of firewood, under rocks he moves from his camp site or makes into a fireplace, or else among plants or vegetable debris. They also have a tendency to creep into his boots, clothing and bedding when left around, and to lurk in crevices of his dwelling.

6

GEOGRAPHICAL DISTRIBUTION
OF DANGEROUS SCORPIONS

The Scorpionida are the most lethal of these terrestrial pests, and in some areas, for instance, North Africa, human deaths from scorpion venom outnumber those caused by poisonous snakes. These fatalities mostly occur among children, but they demonstrate to campers, surveyors, archaeologists, botanists and others the danger of carelessly moving stones, logs, or plant debris in country inhabited by venomous scorpion species. Fortunately, there are many areas where the local scorpions are either too small, or have their poison glands undeveloped.

Scorpions have a general similarity of structure, from the smallest species, such as *Microbuthus opusillus* of Aden, which is about three quarters of an inch in length, to the largest, such as *Palamnaeus longimanus,* of the Philippines, which may grow to eight inches. They have a segmented thick stumpy sausage shaped body, which is supported by four pairs of walking legs. Anteriorly, there is a pair of jointed leg-like pedipalps which terminate in a pincer-like 'hand' (similar to the front claws of crabs and lobsters). At the posterior end of the body is the thin flexible tail of five segments, which carries at its extremity a sharp hollow sting connected to a pair of poison glands in a bulb-like base, termed the telson.

For practical purposes, there are two kinds of scopion sting; (i) which is painful like that of a bee or wasp, and (ii) which is not only painful but also toxic, with effects similar to the injection of 'cobra' venom.

Scorpions are consistently distributed throughout the warm and hot zones of the world, or approximately south of 45° — 40°N. Latitude, though absent from Patagonia, New Zealand and most of the Oceanic Islands. They tend to be solitary creatures, since they either avoid each other or fight to the death. They are normally cannibalistic, but have to suppress this instinct when the two sexes meet at mating time. Several together usually means that the young have not dispersed from the breeding area. Scorpions become sluggish in cold weather and may hibernate or aestivate under adverse conditions. Their distribution and habits are best understood by reference to their supposed origin and ancestral way of life. Scorpions seem to have changed very little since they first crept out of warm northern seas to crush the bodies and suck the juices of the shrimp – or mite-like creatures which were feeding on the debris formed from the first land plants in the Jurassic (scorpion fossils are first found in the Silurian of Europe and North America). Probably they were then, as they are now, nocturnal creatures, using their few simple eyes more to avoid the light than for finding prey, and spent the day (as they still do), hidden in carefully selected microclimates, either in natural rock crevices or in sandy hollows excavated by themselves. Here, partly because of their poor sight, they largely relied on prey coming to them, without the necessity of hunting for it. This is a habit retained by many present-day species, which depend on the sensitive hairs of the forwardly pointing pincers to inform their owner of the approach of living food (crickets, beetles, small lizards and the like) as soon as it comes within seizing range. Some scorpions such as *Euscorpius* (Europe) and *Palamnaeus* (Philippines) rarely use their sting to paralyze their prey, reserving this weapon for defence. Other scorpions, such as *Buthus occitanus, Scorpio maurus,* and *Androctonus australis* (all from north Africa) will repeatedly stab with their sting, either at their living prey, or at anyone who irritates them.

Recession of the order from north of its present limit has probably been caused by glaciation and present winter cold, although there are scorpions which live as high as 9,000 feet, hibernating under the snow until the hot weather returns. Their hypothetical southwards spread through the whole of Africa, (including Madagascar), to northern South America, (at a time when those continents were believed to be joined), may have continued until the South American forms reached Australia, including Tasmania, by way of an Antarctic land-bridge. Scorpions never reached the islands of New Zealand and Oceania, however, as these were already cut off by deep water. There was, though, nothing to prevent the colonizing of all southern Asia, including India, Indo-China, Indonesia and the large islands of the Far East from New Guinea to Japan. During this world-wide expansion, species evolved that were able to exist in the different climates found in warm and hot countries. The medically important present day descendants of these species may therefore roughly be divided into two kinds; those able to live in hot dry areas (semi-desert and desert), and those which live in the humid tropics.

Scorpions are able to endure long periods of starvation. The large *Hadrurus* species of North America are able to survive four to nine months without food or water. *Tityus trinitatis* of Trinidad and Brazil can forego food for three to four months provided water is available. *Buthus occitanus* of south eastern Europe and North Africa can starve for over a year.

Although it is impractical to classify the six families and four hundred known species, yet, since information on scorpions is so difficult to obtain, it is essential to give data on some of the most important forms, if the entomologist is to discuss scorpionism with a zoologist, a medical officer or an Institute producing specific antivenines.

The small dark coloured *Euscorpius* of southern Europe are not dangerous, and it is sometimes necessary to repeat this, since these creatures are often carried in baggage to various parts of the world and usually create alarm when discovered. These scorpions, however, never seem to colonize, unlike *Isometrus maculatus,* a medium sized yellow dark-spotted scorpion which has widely distributed itself *via* ships throughout the tropical and subtropical regions. It is not a dangerous species, and neither is the European variety of the yellowish *Buthus occitanus* (only active in hot weather), though the larger form of this species found in North Africa is listed among the venomous species.

Along the southern (north African) and eastern portion (to Iraq and the Persian Gulf) of the Mediterranean coastal region, however, three very dangerous scorpion species occur; (1) the medium sized yellowish *Androctonus australis,* the sting of which can kill a man in four hours, and a dog (a very susceptible animal, unlike hedgehogs, jerboas and fennec foxes), in seven minutes (scorpion poison typically acts with more severity on cold-blooded arthropods than on warm-blooded animals). This 'fat-tailed' scorpion is specially adapted for dry conditions though it does not avoid water. It is the most dangerous of the

North Africa species, and stings are common amongst the native population, causing a high percentage of deaths in children. Specific antivenin is prepared by the Institute Pasteur d'Algiers, Algeria; (2) *Scorpio maurus* also has a wide range, being found from the Atlantic to India. On the southern Atlas slopes and plateaux it is found in company with the common yellow Mediterranean scorpion *Buthus occitanus,* as well as on the plains of Iraq. It is not considered as dangerous as *Androctonus australis,* and neutralising antivenin is prepared by the Institute Pasteur d'Algerie. (3) Over the same terrain, but focussing in the Sudan and Upper Egypt, though also common in Israel and Syria, is the large yellow sand-scorpion *Buthus* (= *Leirus) quinquestriatus,* which causes over 50% mortality in the many children stung each year. It is particularly dangerous because of the large dose and high toxicity contained in the telson. Antivenin is produced by the State Serum and Vaccine Institute, Agouza, Cairo, Egypt.

In the Middle East (Turkey, Iraq, Iran to the Red Sea Coast) *Buthus crassicauda* is the commonest cause of stings, and is responsible for the death of numerous children. Antivenin is produced by Refik Saydan, Central Institute of Hygiene, Ankara, Turkey.

In Manchuria and North China *Buthus martensi* is the most frequent source of stings.

South of the African Sahara, in the drier areas, *Androctonus australis* remains the most lethal of the scorpions, although *Buthus* (= *Leirus) quinquestriatus* is common, but in the more humid forest regions of the West Coast and Congo and some drier areas extending to South Africa, the very large imperial scorpion *Pandinus imperator* causes the native population to be in considerable dread of it because of the size and severity of its sting, the effect of which may cause temporary or permanent paralysis. In Liberia the Thew-hip scorpion *Titanodamen bassemensis,* which may reach six inches in length is reported to give severe stings. In southern Africa, the species of *Parabuthus* are considered sufficiently venomous to warrant special antivenin. This is produced by the South African Institute for Medical Research, Johannesburg. In this part of Africa it is believed that scorpions are most venomous during the mating season which is between September and January.

In the Indian and Malayan Oriental regions species of *Tamulus* and *Palamnaeus* are considered the most dangerous, although there are many other species of scorpions able to cause inconvenience by their stings. The large *Pandinus* of tropical Africa differ from the tropical Asian large *Palaminaeus* in the structure of a ventrally placed hissing or stridulating organ. No scorpion antivenin for this area seems to be available.

In the western and southwestern dry areas of North America, including northern Mexico, the very dangerous genus *Centruroides* occurs. The most notorious species is the "durango" *Centruroides suffusus* which is reported to have killed 1,600 persons in 36 years. It is found chiefly in northern Mexico (including the state of Durango), and kills many children every year, as well as a number of old people and young adults. In the United States, only *Centruroides sculpturatus* and *Centruroides gertschi* are considered lethal (most stings are reported from Arizona), and it is said that the lethal species are called "bark-scorpions" because they lurk in the loose bark of trees, the non-lethal forms being "ground-scorpions" that live in sand or under objects and only accidentally are found in dwellings. These latter, however, cause severe local pain and swelling. The symptoms of serious scorpion stings are:- severe pain, tightness of the throat, speech difficulty, restlessness and twitching of the muscles, sneezing and salivation, increased heart rate, convulsions, and blue extremities followed by death. This has occurred within forty-five minutes to twelve hours after the sting.

Hadrurus hirsutus is a large and hairy species to be avoided in the south eastern and other parts of the United States (including California).

It appears that no scorpion antivenin is produced in the United States, but the Laboratories Myn, Av. Coyoacan 1707, Mexico 12, D.F., produce a neutralizing serum against the Mexican *Centruroides suffusus, Centruroides noxius* (uncommon in Arizona, but 12 times as toxic as the durango), *Centruroides limpidus, Centruroides limpidus tecumanus* (very potent), *Centruroides limpidus infamatus* and *Centruroides sculpturatus.*

The foregoing scorpions have been species adjusted to dry areas, but from Central America to the southern aspect of the

Amazon basin the hot humid forest-lands harbour scorpion species which prefer this environment.

The family Bothriuridae, which is mainly American (though one genus *Cercophonius* is found in Australia) may be recognised by the white patch of membrane just behind the base of the sting. One species is *Bothriurus bonariensis*, which is often found in baths and around kitchens within doors, as well as in gardens and refuse piles. It is a venomous species. The best known dangerous scorpions of this region, however, belong to the genus *Tityus*, of which the common yellow *Tityus serrulatus* (45 deaths from 1,328 stings in Bello Horizonte, Brazil) and the dark red *Tityus bahiensis*, are the most notorious.

These scorpions tend to walk around gardens and the rooms of houses at night, searching for spiders and cockroaches. They always seek shelter from the daylight, however, and will readily enter small boxes made of black paper if these are left in corners for them. In this way they are easily captured. These, and other scorpions, are particularly likely to enter buildings and dwellings during the rainy season, when their usual hide-outs become flooded. At these times they frequently crawl into clothing or footwear. A rarer species *Tityus trivittatus* has venom as toxic as that of *Tityus serrulatus*.

Tityus cambridgei is a large blackish-brown venomous scorpion which is common from Panama to Brazil. Another blackish species that commonly causes severe poisoning on the Island of Trinidad and in mainland Brazil is *Tityus trinitatis* (25% mortality in children). Antivenin against *Tityus serrulatus* and *Tityus bahiensis* is produced by the Institute Butantan Caixa Postal 65, Sao Paulo, Brazil. Epidemics of scorpionism have occurred as far south as Buenos Aires Province, Argentina, during periods of hay handling and cereal bag loading.

There are no reliable reports of lethal scorpions from Australia, although stinging species abound. There is, however, one authentic case of a baby being killed by an unknown species.

7

GEOGRAPHICAL DISTRIBUTION
OF VENOMOUS CENTIPEDES

Carnivorous Centipedes (order Chilopoda = lip-feet), which may give a venomous bite, must not be confused with vegetarian millipedes (order Diplopoda = double feet), which are comparatively harmless to man (though some species secrete a very irritating fluid). Both orders have long segmented forms that at first glance might appear similar. Millipedes, however, have an almost circular section and a ventral fringe of short thin legs which are arranged two pairs to each segment. Centipedes, on the other hand, have somewhat flattened segments with well separated stout legs, one on either side of each segment. Millipedes 'flow' slowly along the ground, whilst centipedes (if the weather is warm enough to suit their metabolism), tend to 'run' rapidly.

There are centipede species in all the temperate climates, which shelter under logs and damp stones during the day, and come forth to hunt small arthropods at night. The largest of these is perhaps *Lithobius fasciatus* of Austria and Italy, which grows to about two and a half inches. It is harmless to man.

'Giant' species, however, abundantly inhabit the tropics and sub-tropics, and their preference is for areas of high temperature linked with high humidity. In this kind of environment they attain frightening sizes, the largest centipede species probably being *Scolopendra giganta*, of Jamaica, Trinidad, and South America. This grows to eleven or more inches in length.

Each major tropical region has its 'giant' centipedes, which inspire dread in the local populations. In Africa *Ethmostigmus trigonopodus* is perhaps the largest and commonest. South Asia has *Scolopendra subspinipes* (introduced into many tropical seaports by shipping, but unable to colonize temperate areas such as England), and Australia has *Ethmostigmus rubripes*.

All these large centipedes are difficult to keep out of camps, for not only are they active wanderers and climbers during the hours of darkness, when they will attack mice, spiders, or any living thing they are able to overcome (except snakes and toads), but before dawn they like to crawl under or into baggage and stores, so as to sleep in the crevices of boxes or folds of material during the following day.

When hunting, the movements of centipedes are not unlike those of a snake, and the turning speed of the forward part of their body when they sense prey or danger is similar to that of a snake when striking. The head and adjacent segments will swing or whip around in a manner too fast to follow, and the sharp pointed front pair of legs which are just below the head will in an instant seize, pierce and venomize any soft-bodied creature. It is this greatly developed hollow sharply pointed first pair of legs that gives rise to the name of the Order (*chilos*, lip; *pous*, foot). An opening at their tips enables venom from the poison glands to enter the bite punctures.

'Giant' centipedes will climb (with the aid of their very sharp single claws at the tip of their many legs), up the insides of tents in order to be near the ventilation holes at the top, where the insects attracted by the light tend to fly. Here they will attach by their hind legs and swing the body and head swiftly to seize such prey the moment it comes within reach.

Campers are often bitten when they are asleep, by centipedes climbing among the bed-clothes. The intensity of pain produced by these attacks lasts for about half an hour, though it may take some three weeks for the part to return to normal. Fever may occur for several days after a bite. While the death of an adult human has never been recorded from a centipede bite, there is an authentic record of a child dying twenty-nine hours after receiving a bite on the head. The species responsible was believed to have been *Scolopendra subspinipes*. Local anaesthetic injected as soon as possible after the bite can greatly relieve the initial pain.

8

GEOGRAPHICAL DISTRIBUTION
OF VENOMOUS SPIDERS

It has long been known that the Californian Indians poisoned their arrow heads with the bruised bodies of Po'ko-moo, the small black spider with the red hour-glass marking on the belly. Only in recent years, however, has it been accepted that there are several kinds of spiders able to deliver lethal bites to humans. This late recognition of the danger of venomous spider bites was probably due to the unmasking of the medium-sized brown European *Lycosa tarentula*, which was once widely supposed to cause Tarantism (including a hysterical desire to dance continually) by its bite, but has since been proved not to be dangerous.

The myth regarding the only known venomous European spider having been exploded, a tendency arose to disbelieve the persistent reports of native populations in various parts of the world that there were other dangerous spiders. Even the big birdeating Megalomorphae became generally accepted as 'harmless", whereas some of them can cause dreadful necrosis of tissue over large areas of the body. It is also not generally realised that some of these large jungle species have a covering of beautiful thick hair resembling fur, the touching of which may cause susceptible persons to develop severe allergic urticaria, thus demonstrating a natural defence on the part of the spider to protect itself against various vertebrate foes.

The jungle folk of Indo-China, however, eat both the giant orb-web *Nephila* (= the 'golden one', and the largest web builder) and large hairy *Mygalomorpha*, after pulling out the chelicerae, and roasting the bodies on sticks to singe off the hair. As is the case with roasted or fried locusts, they are excellent when eaten with salt.

The various kinds of venomous spiders have a world-wide distribution, being found in temperate, subtropical and tropical regions. Their ancestors, which first appear in Devonian times,

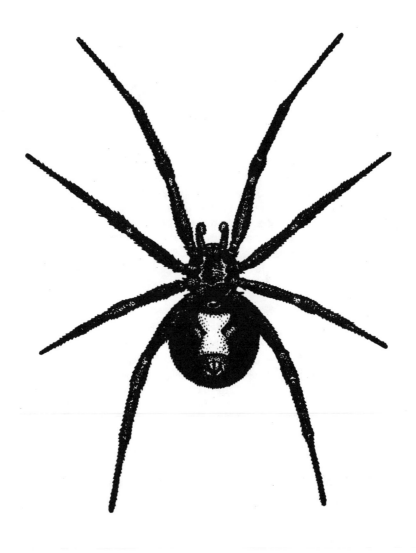

Fig. 26 Black widow spider *Latrodectus mactans*. The hour-glass marking on the black ventral aspect of the female abdomen is coloured red in nature.

had by the Carboniferous period secured for themselves a very wide dispersal, and today spiders are found in higher latitudes, at higher altitudes and on more distant islands (e.g. New Zealand and Hawaii) than either scorpions or snakes. Some even live between the tide marks of warm seas *(Desis)*. They are all carnivorous and imbibe fluid food only. The typical method of feeding is to puncture the integument of their prey with their sharply pointed hollow chelicerae or fangs, inject a paralysing venom, and then, when the victim is subdued, to pour digestive fluid into the fang punctures, which after breaking down the soft parts, is sucked back through the mouth opening of the spider into the alimentary tract.

The hall-mark of the spiders is their ability to produce and manipulate silk threads. Most spiders, even the primitive species, make a tunnel of silk which is capable of various uses, one being a microclimate in which to sleep or hibernate out of the wet, cold or wind. Spiders of temperate regions are generally of smaller size, and of shorter life than those native to tropical regions, where some species have a leg-span of seven inches and may live for several years.

The most widespread genus of those dangerous to man is *Latrodectus* (Fig. 26), which has various geographical species, subspecies and varieties, all of which are highly venomous. The best known is the North and South American *Latrodectus mactans,* (the venom of which, drop for drop, is more lethal than that of any species of rattlesnake), and the various kinds of which are found from southern Canada to Chile (where it is widely distributed and known as 'vientre colorado' or 'red belly'). The North American geographical forms are *Latrodectus mactans* (eastern and central states from New Hampshire to Florida and westwards to Texas and Oklahoma); *Latrodectus mactans texanus* (south-western states — commonest in Texas, and westwards to California; north to Utah, and south to Mexico); and *Latrodectus mactans hesperus* (common in all states west of the Rockies, from southern Canada to northern Texas).

Latrodectus mactans, usually known as the "Black Widow" spider, is of frequent occurrence in the rubbish dumps of New York city. Its web is placed near the ground beneath large-sized timber and waste-paper material. These spiders tend to migrate and redistribute themselves in the autumn (probably in relation to hibernation), and inhabit almost any shelter that is warm and dry.

The female *Latrodectus mactans* is the venomous sex (the males are very small) and lives for about one year. She is particularly aggressive when guarding her egg-sac (containing some 600 young), which is often placed under the wooden seat of a garden privy. She is black in colour with a globular shaped hind-body that may reach one centimetre in width, and is quite unmistakable when turned over to display the ventral surface, which bears a bright red hour-glass marking.

These comparatively small but highly venomous *Latrodectus* spiders have different names in different geographical areas. Some of these are as follows: *Latrodectus hasseltii,* the "Redback" spider, which is sometimes regarded as the Far Eastern equivalent of the American *Latrodectus mactans* or Blackwidow spider. Both forms are similar in general appearance, though *hasseltii* typically has a red or orange stripe down the back of the hind body and the ventral hour-glass marking is usually much less complete than on *mactans.* This spider has a very wide distribution, including Australia; New Zealand (where it is known as the 'Katipo' = 'night-stinger', and is common on the beaches of North Island but less so on South Island); New Caledonia; Timor; New Guinea; Maldives; New Hebrides; Philippines; Marianas; Borneo; Ishigaki (Ryukyu Islands) and many other islands.

Where the Red-back widow *(Latrodectus hasseltii)* overlaps with the Continental Asian species of *Latrodectus,* it is often difficult to determine the species, because of colour variation and the close relationship of the main kinds.

Latrodectus geometricus, the "Grey Widow" spider, is geographically found between the Western *mactans* and the Far Eastern *hasseltii.* It is a semi-tropical and tropical species and varies in colour from light yellow to almost black. The ventral 'hour-glass' is invariably present, and the spider typically carries small pale geometric designs on the back of the hind-body. It has been observed in Australia, Hawaii, India, North and South America, and the southern half of Africa. On the whole, the venom from its bite seems less toxic than that of *mactans,* or that of its outdoor partner *Latrodectus indistinctus (geometricus* prefers buildings though it is common in summer among the vines during the grape harvest). *Latrodectus indistinctus*, though typically South African, may also occur in the Indian Orient, and causes much trouble among the wheat harvesters of Western Province and the Eastern Orange Free State, where it is known as the 'Knoppie' or "Button-spider'. Its venom is much more potent than that of *geometricus*.

Madagascar has its own species, *Latrodectus menavodi*, and northern coastal Africa has *Latrodectus schuchi*, the "bou siha", regarding which no fatalities have been reported. Southern Europe, (including parts of Italy and all Yugoslavia) has *Latrodectus tredecimguttatus*, which is also widely distributed in southern Russia and the Mediterranean region in general. The Corsicans call their island form of *Latrodectus* the "malmignatte".

A "Red-legged Widow" spider *Latrodectus bishopi* occurs in southern Florida. The hairy legs and bare forebody are bright reddish brown. The abdomen is black with four bright red spots. The ventral surface has a partly orange partly yellow triangular spot unlike the brick red hour-glass *mactans*. The venom is believed to be less toxic than that of the black-Widow spider.

A bite from one of the *Latrodectus* spiders usually means great pain (which cannot be alleviated by analgesics and sedatives), followed by muscular cramps and vomiting. These symptoms may last for two to five days, or may continue into shock, respiratory difficulty with raised blood pressure and finally death. Local necrosis of tissue is not usual following *Latrodectus* bites, unless the bite-punctures become secondarily infected, and the field naturalist should be careful not to don clothes in which a 'widow' has taken shelter during the night.

Antivenin against *Latrodectus mactans* venom is produced by Merck-Sharp and Dohme, Philadelphia, Pa.; against *Latrodectus tredecimguttatus* and *Latrodectus hasseltii* by the Central Institute of Hygiene, Zagreb, Yugoslavia; and against *Latrodectus indistinctus* and *Latrodectus geometricus* by the South African Institute for Medical Research.

Southern America has a genus *Loxosceles*, which contains several dangerous species, with venom possibly more toxic than that of *Latrodectus*. There is usually an area of necrosis and haemolysis around the bite in typical cases (healing with a scar in about ten weeks), which may, however, develop into more generalised symptoms ending in death. The best known of this genus is *Loxosceles laeta*, a common house-spider in Peru, Chile, Uruguay and parts of the Argentine. Its body is about 1.5 cm. in length and of a yellow brown colour, with long hairy legs. It hides in crevices of old houses, behind pictures and furniture, and in clothing. It attacks when irritated. *Loxosceles rufipes* is another dangerous species existing side by side with *laeta*. In the southern states of the U.S.A. *Loxosceles reclusa* is a proved cause of loxoscelism. A Marine bitten in a shed in Missouri took three months to recover from one of its bites and required a skin graft to mend the ulcer-crater.

In the humid forest-country of the New World there are many large hairy venomous hunting spiders or "Tarantulas". *Lycosa erythrognatha* and *Lycosa raptoria* are the best known. Their bites cause extensive ulceration and sloughing together with gangrene, as well as occasionally more serious systemic effects.

A dangerous and common hunting species from Brazil and some of the West Indian Islands, which is occasionally exported to other countries in cargoes of fruit, especially bananas, is *Phoneutria fera*. It is a medium-sized spider of a light brown colour with some cream dots, and has long hairy legs. These spiders usually live for five or six years, and are solitary, very aggressive and kill their prey with a venom which drop for drop equals that of the southern diamond-back rattlesnake or 'Casabel', and is only slightly less toxic than venom from the scorpion *Tityus serrulatus*.

Antivenin against *Lycosa* and *Phoneutria* species is produced by the Institute Butantan, Sao Paulo, Brazil.

In the grape-growing country of Peru and the Argentine, the 'Podadora', *Glyptocranium gasteracanthoides*, sometimes termed the 'pruning' spider, is dangerous to the vineyard workers, who in mild cases have to take a week or fortnight off work, and in severe cases suffer generalised symptoms ending in death. It is particularly dangerous to be bitten on the throat.

A very venomous, but geographically restricted species is the Sydney 'Funnel-web'. spider, *Atrax robustus*, a medium sized, brown, heavily-bodied 'tarantula'-like trap-door species found only in the environs of Sydney, New South Wales, Australia. These spiders may give a series of superficial bites, or grasp firmly with the legs and drive in the chelicerae with sufficient force to pierce the skull of a chicken. The females have two and a half times the quantity of venom carried by the males, which however, have the more toxic venom. The prognosis for humans bitten by females is good, but for those bitten by males it is bad, and death usually occurs within a few hours (male spiders typically have the short pair of leg-like palps on either side of the jaws broadened out (swollen) to form a sperm receptaculum. This makes them comparatively easily to recognise).

In Southern Africa the genus *Harpactirella* occurs, with four species restricted to this geographical area. *Harpacterella lightfooti* is the best known, and is a large hunting spider with formidable fangs found among rocks, fallen timber and debris. Its bites are considered dangerous, and the spider should not be confused with its likeness, the non-venomous *Harpactirea bavianna* ("Bobbe jaaspinnekop").

Further north in tropical Africa, there is a host of potentially dangerous spiders, about which little is known, as is the case with the Amazonian forest spiders. African examples of possibly dangerous species which are feared by the natives are *Scodra griseipes, Scodra brachypodes, Heteroscodra crassipes, Hysterocrates didymus, Phoneyusa bidentata.*

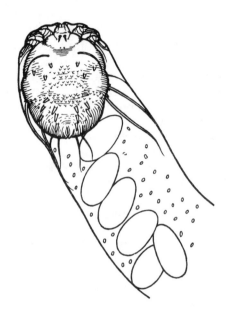

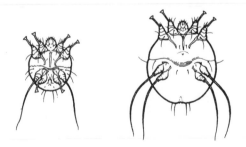

Fig. 27 Scabies mite *Sarcoptes scabiei* laying eggs in a burrow in human skin (top) with adult male (bottom left) and female (bottom right)

9

GEOGRAPHICAL DISTRIBUTION OF MITES AND TICKS OF MEDICAL IMPORTANCE

Mites, as the name implies, are typically small. Their ancestors probably go back to the Jurassic, where they fed on the residues of the first land plants. Their structure is comparatively simple, being a sac-like body in which they store fluid food, with four pairs of legs for locomotion, and a mouth-opening aided by one pair of jaws and one pair of palps.

Their kinds and numbers of individuals are legion, and among their many specialisations are some forms which share man's stored food products or attach to his skin in order to obtain nutriment, while the most important medically are those species which transmit pathogenic organisms. The geographical dispersal of these mites has mostly been arranged by man himself, albeit inadvertently, for he has either carried them from person to person, or made it possible for them to be transported on the bodies of his domestic followers — houseflies, mice and rats.

Man's most constant mite parasite is the Scabies itch mite, *Sarcoptes scabiei hominis* (Fig. 27), which for thousands of years has burrowed beneath the horny layers of his skin, and bred and distributed itself by the personal contact between one person and another. When these mites infest a fresh human host they have three weeks or so to dig their burrows in the skin before the host becomes allergic to their presence, and begins to rid himself of some of them by scratching violently, which activity usually introduces secondary infections that combine to cause the inflammatory condition known as "scabies'. This disease is analogous to the sarcoptic mange of animals. It is most fortunate that modern chemical treatment can cure scabies, as it is almost impossible for a sufferer to obtain sleep during the acute stage. The geographical distribution of these mites is everywhere that man himself goes, except where he maintains the highest standard of personal hygiene and care with his contacts.

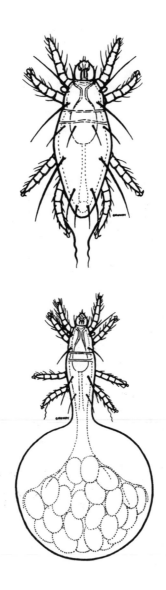

Fig. 28 Straw-itch mite *(Pyemotes ventricosus)* normal adult female (top) and gravid female (bottom).

A number of other mites cause serious allergic dermatitis in man. One such is the Straw- or Grain- itch mite *Pyemotes (= Pediculoides) ventricosus* (Fig. 28), which occurs wherever man harvests and stores grain crops. These mites are normally predaceous on other mites or the grubs of grain-infesting insects, but when this natural food runs short, as it may in the straw of mattresses, the ungravid females readily attack the skin of man, which reacts with a show of allergic dermatitis. These newly fertilised females are eliptical in shape and look like grass seeds adhering to the skin. Apart from destroying those attached to the body, it is essential to trace the source of the infestation, either in straw or grain sacks, and have this destroyed, or removed from proximity.

A group of mites the individuals of which are only just visible to the naked eye is that of the 'Forage-mites'; *Acarus, Tyrophagus* (Fig. 29), and *Glycyphagus* are well known genera of the complex. They specialise in breaking down stored food products such as flour, biscuits, cheese, sugar, bacon, vanilla and copra, and when left to breed in a suitably warm temperature at the correct humidity, will multiply so that the food supply is reduced to a heap of mites of all stages, plus debris. Sometimes food infested in this manner is eaten by humans, either in the raw state as in cheeses, or cooked as in porridge. To those unaccustomed to a mite diet, the ingesting of such material may cause alarming intestinal disturbance, as the mite bodies still retain the enzymes which they used to digest their own food, and these may adversely affect the human alimentary tract.

Sometimes it is necessary to assist in the harvesting of infested grain crops, or the removal of a cereal or other cargo in sacks from ship to shore or *vice versa*, so that for several days the bare arms and other parts of the handler's body are exposed to food dust and attendant mites. The continued presence of this kind of mite on the skin of susceptible persons will quickly lead to allergic dermatitis, which, however, will quickly mend when the causal agents are removed, as for instance when the work is finished, but which will return, even years later, if the bodies of the mites, their faeces, or their cast skins be allowed to make contact with the new sensitized person.

These slow-moving, soft-skinned, tiny, pearl-like creatures have an ingenious method of distributing themselves to new

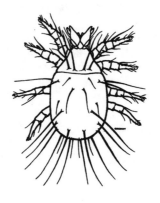

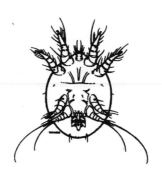

Fig. 29 Forage mite *Tyrophagus* sp. adult (top) and hypopus stage (bottom).

supplies of food, for, under certain conditions, a number of the nymphal forms become thicker-skinned and immobile, while developing suckers on the ventral surface. If a housefly or a mouse or rat contact them in this hypopus stage, the suckers seize on to the hairs of these mobile creatures and in a short time the wings of the housefly or the legs of the mouse or rat will convey the mites to a new supply of stored food. Here the suckers relax, the hypopus moults its skin, and shortly after it will become an adult mite.

Neither *Sarcoptes* nor *Tyrophagus* mites suck the blood of man, for itch-mites ingest the skin-cells of their host when already partly digested outside their bodies, and forage mites cause an allergic condition due to their secretions.

There are blood- and lymph-sucking mites, however, which normally parasitize mice, rats and birds, including pigeons and poultry. When these natural hosts become too heavily infested, or die, or are suddenly removed by epidemic disease, pest control schemes, or transference from their usual haunts, then those mites which have been left behind will swarm on to the nearest warm-blooded host, which may be man. This happens all the more readily since the mites spend most of their time in the nests or sleeping places of the hosts, only attaching themselves when hungry for a blood-meal. The mites most usually incriminated are the rat mite *Liponyssus* (= *Ornithonyssus*) *bacoti*, the fowl- and wild-bird mite *Liponyssus bursa*, and another bird-mite *Dermanyssus gallinae*. These, together with the mouse-mite *Allodermanyssus sanguineus*, may be responsible for severe urticarial dermatitis in man, and the last named is also important as the vector of a typhus-like disease named "rickettsial-pox". In old houses and caves, bat-mites such as *Liponyssus flavus*, may cause dermatitis by biting persons who use them for shelter. The geographical distribution of these rodent- and avian-mites is as widespread as their hosts, which in turn are dependent on the distribution of man.

The genus *Trombicula*, which contains the 'harvest mites' and 'harvest bugs' that infest man all over the world, causes a condition variously known as "scrub itch", "harvest-itch", "redbug itch" etc. The lesions are caused by the habit of the mite when in the larval parasitic stage, of attaching itself to the host's skin with its pair of chelicerae, and then pouring out a digestive saliva which bores a tube directly into the skin-cells of the host. Down this tube the larva sucks nutrient fluid (not blood). Meanwhile, the skin reacts with a characteristic granulation and inflammation that invites scratching and the introduction of secondary infections. Multiple bites are usual, as the mite larvae having recently hatched from eggs on the ground, swarm along paths, rat-runs in vegetation, and around the mouths of rodent burrows, searching for a warm-blooded host. An explorer pushing his way through bushes or grasses, or lying down in mite 'islands', will shortly afterwards find his body literally covered in allergic reactions to their bites. Fortunately, these larval parasites do not usually find the taste of human skin satisfactory, and invariably drop-off before the tube-making process is completed. Entomologists who would like to observe the tubes for themselves, should kill a rat in a district where the mites occur and examine the inside of the ears. Here the mite larvae, if present, will be found clustering together to form an orangecoloured patch, always in a position that cannot be scratched by their host, each individual larva being attached to the tube from which it sucks the exudate that will gradually fill out its sac-like body over a period of some four or five days.

If the mites are pulled away with forceps, and particularly if the mouths of the now exposed tubes in the skin are cleaned with spirit, these will show their hole or tunnel-like structure, so that the area from which the larvae have been removed will appear to be honeycombed with deep punctures.

The inflammatory raised areas caused by the attachment of the young mites to human hosts will subside in a day or so after the parasites have been removed and the bites bathed in antiseptic or cooling lotion. This is so long as the digestive saliva did not contain pathogenic organisms such as typhus rickettsiae, for if it had, the bite spot would later break down into an eschar.

Although *Trombicula* mite larvae are responsible for much urticaria in the many countries around the world which are infested with them, it is only in one large but limited geographical area of the Far East that two species of these mites, *Trombicula akamushi* and *Trombicula deliensis*, are vectors of the rickettsiae that cause mite-borne typhus, known as "Japanese River fever" in Japan, 'scrub-typhus' (Fig. 30) in Burma and Malaya, 'Sumatran-mite fever' in Sumatra, and 'coastal

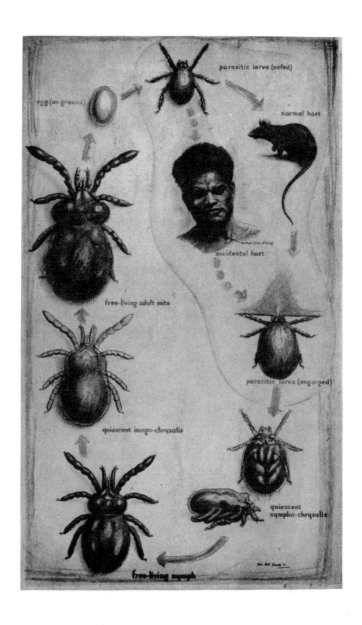

Fig. 30 Life-cycle of *Trombicula* mite, vector of scrub typhus. Only the larval stage is parasitic.

fever' in Queensland, Australia (Fig. 27). Similar diseases occur in IndoChina and the Philippines. The geographical area of infection is bounded on the north by the Kumaon Hills of India and the dry lands of northern China, but includes southern Japan, while the southern boundary is south and west of the humid northern and eastern coasts of Australia. The Western limits are the coastal areas of eastern India and include Ceylon, Malaya, Sumatra, and Java, while the eastern boundary includes New Guinea and the Solomons.

Sporadically scattered over this vast area are groups of rodents and birds which act as reservoirs of the rickettsiae, and carriers of the infected mite larvae. Since, however, the mite adults, although not parasitic, can pass the rickettsiae through the egg stage to following generations, the unfed mites just out of the egg may readily infect a human venturing into their territory.

Terrain particularly to be avoided is 'secondary jungle', *i.e.* land which has been used by villagers for agricultural purposes, and then allowed to revert. This means that rats have been left behind when the village moved on, for although scrub-palm, bamboo-thicket, acacia-scrub, sorghum-grass and creeping-bracken may now occupy the area where tall trees were once dominant, the rats and their possibly infected mite parasites may still be present.

Secondary jungle is attractive to weary naturalists looking for a place to camp in a tangled jungle area, for it is easy to cut back and clear, but unless it is known to be free of typhus mites, secondary jungle should always be avoided. If it is essential to explore mite-typhus country, then all clothing must be regularly smeared with mite-repellent.

Whilst mites are invariably small (the only large form of medical importance being the hard-shelled 'Red-poison mite' of Mauritius, which when handled, leaves sufficient toxic secretion on the fingers to cause the mouth and throat to swell dangerously if the lips are touched), ticks are comparatively large, even the young ones just out of the egg-shell being much bigger and easier to see than the average full grown scabies, straw-itch- or forage-mites. These tough skinned mite-like ticks feed on blood only and are external parasites of both cold- and warm-blooded animals, including man. They are of two distinct kinds, and it is important to differentiate between them, since the one kind, the so-called "Soft ticks", is concerned with the transmission of spirochaetes causing relapsing fever; while the other kind, the so-called (Hard tics) includes the vecdors of dhe rickettsiae that cause tick-borne typhus.

"Soft ticks", the more generalised form, are 'ticks of the habitat', for, like bed-bugs, they spend most of their time sleeping in crevices or sand near the resting places of their animal hosts. Unless driven by hunger or special circumstances to feed by day, they are nocturnal, and only come out to suck blood at night when their hosts are comfortably asleep. If occupying continuously used sleeping or resting quarters, such as animal-inhabited areas, native rest-houses, small oases, or tree shade used by large animals, they are able to feed and moult regularlynd often, and the females will frequently lay eggs in small batches.

To avoid the attentions of soft ticks of the only dangerous genus *Ornithodorus* (Fig. 31), whether they happen to be vectors of relapsing fever spirochaetes or not (for all species of this genus have commensal spirochaetes of their own in their saliva, which if injected into man during the short feeding period, may cause a raised temperature or fever), the naturalist must take care not to sleep near their known 'habitats' such as 'deer beds', caves or regular camping places along caravan routes.

The most important species of the genus *Ornithodorus*, are as follows (the only other soft tick which is likely to be of nuisance value is the Persian pigeon or fowl-tick *Argas persicus*, which can be a real pest when biting at night. It is a Middle Eastern species):-

Ornithodorus moubata, the eyeless tampan, is the most important relapsing fever tick in Africa. It feeds almost exclusively on the blood of man, since it prefers living in village-huts with earth floors and at stopping places along the caravan and migrating labourers' routes. It transmits the infecting spirochaetes *via* its 'coxal fluid', which is a secretion issuing from openings near the bases of the front legs and is composed of the clear portion of the blood separated from the red corpuscles. This fluid pours out around the bite puncture during the act of feeding. Some *Ornithodorus* ticks transmit relapsing fever by way of their anticoagulant saliva, but the majority transmit the

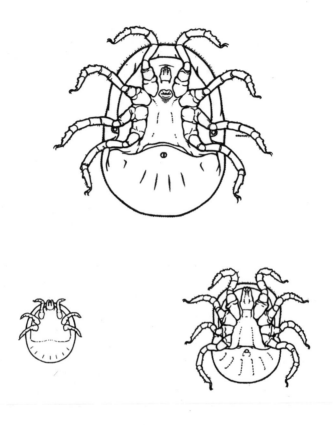

Fig. 31 Soft tick *Ornithodorus* sp. with adult (top), six legged larval stage (bottom left) and eight-legged nymph (bottom right).

organisms *via* the coxal fluid.

Ornithodorus savignyi, the eyed tampan, covers a similar distribution to that of *moubata*, but it is less domestic, and feeds largely on animals resting under shade-trees outdoors. It is a vector of relapsing fever but is not so important as *moubata*.

Ornithodorus pavimentosus is a South African species which gives a severe bite.

Ornithodorus hermsi is found in the north and southwestern U.S.A. (including California) where it feeds on the squirrels and chipmunks of the high altitude woodlands. It is dangerous for anyone to camp near decaying stumps of the Douglas fir *(Pseudotsuga taxifolia)*, in these localities, as they are often the lurking and hibernating 'habitats' of these relapsing fever vectors.

Ornithodorus parkeri seems to prefer open grassy spaces and semi-desert conditions, whether at low altitudes or on 7,000 ft. plateaus (Wyoming). It is mainly a western species, and feeds on prairie rodents and even on the burrowing owl *(Speotyto cunicularia)*. It seems to be widely infected and has been recorded as a relapsing fever vector in California.

Ornithodorus turicata is found in the warmer parts of North America, from Florida to Texas and Mexico. It feeds on most animals, including snakes and terrapins. It is considered dangerous to sleep in the limestone caves of Texas and unwise to camp near colonies of rodents. In Mexico these ticks are a pest of roosting chickens. When infected *Ornithodorus turicata* transmits the spirochaetes rapidly to a human host, very soon after it begins feeding.

Ornithodorus talaje has a wide distribution in the American sub-tropics and tropics. Its range extends from Texas to the Argentine. It feeds on ground-rodents, rats, birds and reptiles. It transmits relapsing fever in Guatemala, Panama and Colombia.

Ornithodorus rudis is the most important vector of relapsing fever in Central and South America. Its range is from Panama to Paraguay. It seems to feed only on man, and is found extensively in village dwellings.

Ornithodorus coriaceus, the large 'pajaroello', is found in parts of California and Mexico. Its 'habitat' is often the sleeping places of wild deer among the scrub oaks. It is known to transmit relapsing fever, but the painful long lasting effects of its bite

99

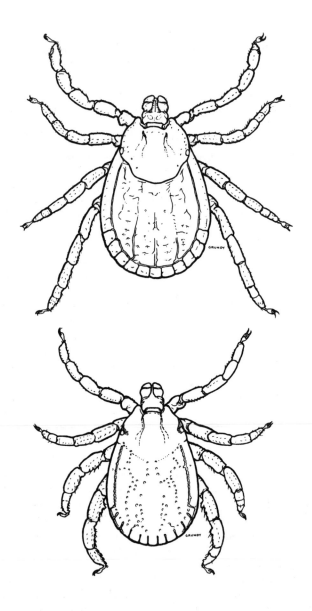

Fig. 32 A hard tick (Ixodidae) female (top) and male (bottom).

cause it to be more feared locally than the rattlesnake.

Ornithodorus rostratus is found in southern Brazil, northern Argentina, Paraguay and Bolivia. It feeds on man in his dwellings and the bite often causes extensive areas of bruising since it appears to inject a powerful anticoagulant.

Ornithodorus brasiliensis is a large species found in Brazil, which gives 'a bite causing serious after effects.

Ornithodorus gurneyi is the only *Ornithodorus* found in Australia. Its bite may cause paralysis, loss of consciousness and blindness.

"Hard Ticks" (Fig. 32) differ in habit from "Soft Ticks" by spending much more time on the host. Instead of both sexes feeding for fifteen minutes to one hour on a sleeping animal or person, as is the case with soft ticks, the larva, nymph and adult female of a hard tick species spend days or weeks attached to their host. The male hard tick will also be found on the host for long periods, but his interest is only to serve the females. Instead of being able to moult at leisure through many life-stages and to lay many small batches of eggs as do the soft ticks, the hard ticks have but one larval stage out of the egg, one intermediate nymphal stage, and the adult male or female stage. This provides the shortest number of moults by means of which a tick can grow from egg to adult.

Sometimes all three stages are spent on one host animal, but usually the fully fed tick drops off its host with each engorgement, and after moulting has to find a new one for the next stage.

Often they have to undergo long periods of starvation before they can meet and attach to a new host, the longest time usually being the hibernation period of the northern ticks, and it is an interesting medical fact that such starved ticks, which may contain rickettsiae in their tissues, cannot infect a human host until a period of from five to eight hours has passed, during which the organisms "reactivate" themselves after the long period of low metabolism in the vector tick.

"Hard ticks" are so named because they always have a shiny shield on the fore-part of their back, which covers the whole dorsal surface of the male (which does not engorge), but only the anterior portion near the false head of the female (which engorges enormously in a direction posterior to the shield).

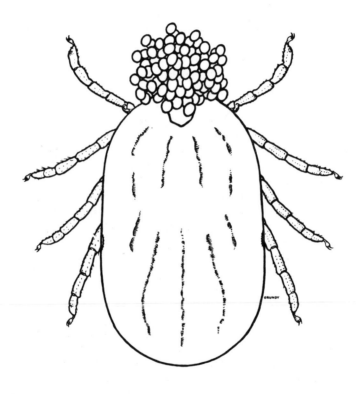

Fig. 33 Fully fed gravid female hard tick in the process of laying eggs. The genital orifice is ventral and just behind the mouth parts.

Attached to the front part of the shield is the false-head which carries the mouth parts. This false-head is terminal and easily seen from above in hard-ticks, while it is ventral and therefore not easily seen from above in soft-tics. Since hard-tics spend so much time on their host, they are often described as "ticks of the hosts" for it is on animals that one looks for them (Fig. 33).

An important procedure for field naturalists to carry out before camping in hard-tick country is to test the proposed camp area by the simple method of trailing a woollen vest or piece of light coloured blanket, which has been tied to a long stick flagwise, over the grass and herbage. Examination of the material every few minutes will soon disclose the absence or presence of hungry hard-ticks, for if these are infesting this particular spot, they will grasp the wool with their long thin claws as it is swept slowly over them and climb on board. The ticks will appear as small dark slowly moving spots on the paler background, and according to their size may be judged to be "seed ticks" (larvae), nymphs, or unfed adults. They will always be small, however, for it is only on the host animal that they become engorged and vastly larger than when unfed. If they are found on the vest or blanket then the camper must move on and try again. Usually ticks are only found in certain areas and valleys, and the precaution described should procure a tick-free site.

The geographical distribution of hard-ticks is world wide, and due to their powers of resistance to long periods of starvation, and to the ability of some genera and species to withstand cold by the careful choosing of humid warm microclimates among matted vegetation during the periods they are not on a host, they are well represented at northerly latitudes in the boreal forest zone, as well as being found throughout the temperate and tropical zones.

An idea of their distribution as regards the transmission of tick-borne typhus may be gained from the following notes on the most important species.

Dermacentor andersoni, the wood tick, is the well known vector of Rocky-mountain spotted fever in the western mountain states of the U.S.A. with an extension into New Mexico. It frequents grass and sage brush areas, and the infection it transmits is typically acquired by explorers, hunters, and farmers who work outdoors. As with all tick-borne fevers, the intensity of the disease seems to vary with the district, but in the foci of Bitter Root Valley and other parts of Montana the mortality has reached 80% with an average of perhaps 40%.

Dermacentor variabilis, the dog tick, is a transmitter of spotted fever in the eastern states of the U.S.A., mostly to women and children. Here again the intensity of the disease varies from district to district and from year to year. The death rate (always lower than in Rocky-mountain fever) is about 25%.

Amblyomma americanum, the lone star tick, ranges from the southern states of the U.S.A. into South America. It is considered a vector of tick-typhus.

Amblyomma cajennense of tropical South America, is the main vector of spotted fever in this region. Various names are given to the disease — Sao Paulo typhus or Brazilian spotted fever and Colombian tick fever, are but three. These ticks are considered to be dangerous vectors associated with a death rate of about 70%.

Rhipicephalus sanguineus, the dog tick, is found in the Mediterranean region and in parts of Africa. It is the vector of fièvre boutonneuse and Kenya tick typhus. The mortality rate of these fevers does not exceed 2%.

In southern Africa, the various kinds of wild animals, including veld rodents, permit parasitizing by several hard-tick species. Some of these convey the rickettsiae of 'tick-bite fever' to man. Examples are *Amblyomma hebraeum* (bont tick), *Boophilus decoloratus* (cattle tick), *Haemaphysalis leachi* (dog tick), and *Rhipicephalus appendiculatus*. This form of typhus lasts about a fortnight and terminates rapidly, with a mortality rate of about 1%.

A condition associated with the prolonged bite of certain hard-tick females when gravid is tick-paralysis. The toxic saliva of these ticks causes an ascending motor paralysis to take place in the host, which ends in death when the respiratory muscles are affected. A number of children and dogs die of this condition every year in rural America and Australia. The most dangerous point for these ticks to adher to is the nuchal hollow at the back of the neck. *Dermacentor andersoni* is one of the 'paralysis ticks'.

Boots and trousers are essential as a protection in tick infested areas, and field workers must make a careful examination of themselves, preferably twice a day, since some hard-ticks do not cause irritation when attaching, and if they can adhere to the head or anal regions they may even reach engorgement before being found. Care must be taken to make the tick remove itself, by means of a hot cigarette end, or else by dissection of the mouth parts from the skin, for if ticks are removed by force, this portion is always left in the bite-puncture where it inevitably festers.

Hard-ticks are partly responsible for the transmission of several other diseases besides typhus. Three examples are tularaemia, bullis fever and Q fever. Also, a role in which hard-tics are becoming important is in the transmission of the various encephalitides, or virus infections of the central nervous system. In warmer parts of the world mosquitoes are considered the main vectors of these diseases, but in more northerly latitudes ticks appear to be harbouring the causal organisms, and a great deal of work is being done on the association of ticks with migratory birds and mammals, in order to solve part of the problem. Russian spring-summer encephalitis, transmitted to man by the hard-tick *Ixodes persulcatus*, which is naturally parasitic on forest rodents, is an example of this group of diseases.

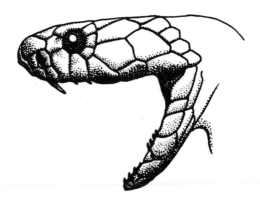

Fig. 34 Head of an elapid snake showing one of the pair of fixed front fangs.

10

GEOGRAPHICAL DISTRIBUTION
OF DANGEROUS SNAKES

There are approximately 2,700 species of non-poisonous, and about 300 species of venomous snakes. These cold-blooded reptiles are widely distributed over most regions of the world, and some species inhabit much more northerly areas than scorpions. For instance, the common viper ranges through northern Europe and Siberia, and the prairie rattlesnake is found as far north as the 50th parallel in Canada.

Field zoologists should know terrain in which they are likely to be bitten by poisonous snakes and if possible should recognise the species or kind of snake involved, and be able to apply any necessary first aid measures.

The distribution and habits of poisonous snakes are most easily understood by examining their supposed evolutionary dispersal.

Snakes are one of the three successful groups of reptiles that carried on into the age of mammals and birds. The other two are the Tortoises (including the tropical sea-turtles *Eretmochelys imbricata*, and *Dermochelys coriacea*, the flesh of which may cause death from twelve hours to two weeks after ingestion), and the Lizards (including crocodiles, and the gila monsters *Heloderma horridum* and *Heloderma suspectum* of the deserts of south western U.S.A. and northern Mexico, which inoculate a lethal venom if allowed to obtain a grip with their toothed jaws).

Whilst Africa has the best show of lizards, tropical Asia owns the greatest variety of snakes, and is unique in having all main venomous types — 'cobra', 'sea-snake', 'viper', and 'pit-viper'.

The earliest snakes were probably non-poisonous dwellers in burrows or crevices (Cretaceous branch of monitor lizards), and either swallowed small cold-blooded prey alive as the common grass-snake does a frog, or else first constricted it to death, as do pythons. They were, of course, aided in swallowing by their ability to disarticulate their jaws when ingesting prey larger than their own diameter. Giant non-venomous constrictor snakes capable of crushing a man exist today in every continent where they can find suitably high temperature, shelter (typically including areas of water to sleep in) and food supplies. Africa has the Rock python, *Python sebae* which grows to 20 feet; IndoChina has the Reticulated python *Python reticulatus* of up to 33 feet, also the Indian and Javan python *Python molurus* which grows to 25 feet; Australia has the Amethystine rock-python *Liasis amethystinus kinghorni* of up to 21 feet; and South America has the Anaconda or water-boa *Eunectes murinus,* of up to 36 feet. Of these giant snakes, however, only anacondas, in the Amazon rain-forest, are likely deliberately to hunt a man in order to eat him.

Certain ancestral snakes (Miocene period) evolved a saliva that proved toxic when inoculated into the blood-stream of their prey. These snakes were at an advantage when struggling with strong or active reptiles, since their technique was to seize with sharp teeth and then hold on and chew until the victim died.

This ancient method is still the basis of the attack made by poisonous cobras, kraits, sea-snakes, coral-snakes, mambas, and all venomous snakes of Australia, and their chemically complex venom is still mainly neurotoxic in effect, which causes a respiratory paralysis that is especially effective against coldblooded creatures. The poison snakes above named all have a pair of fixed fangs in the front of the upper jaw, with a channel along the antero-lateral edge of each, down which venom pours from the poison glands in the cheeks, when these are pressed by the biting muscles.

This kind of snake is believed to have had its origin in the hot seasonally humid regions of the tropical Orient which it is believed once stretched from India to Formosa, and from southern China to Celebes, including the now sunken Sunda shelf.

The modern representatives of the neurotoxic-venomed snakes of this zoological region are as follows: the Indian Krait *(Bungarus caeruleus)* which occurs in the Indus valley, India, Ceylon, and the Ganges valley, where it is a much dreaded snake, growing to four feet in length. It is black in colour with 'ridged' vertebral scales along its back. About 70% of persons bitten by kraits die. The Malayan Krait *(Bungarus candidus)*

Fig. 35 Head of a viperid snake showing one of the pair of hinged front fangs.

occurs in the Malay peninsula and Archipelago. It grows to five feet, is dark with white bands, and the dorsal scales are also 'ridged'. The Banded Krait *(Bungarus fasciatus)* from north-east India, Burma, Malaya and the Archipelago, Thailand, Viet Nam, south China etc., grows to seven feet, and is black with yellow bands, displaying the most 'ridged' vertebral scales of all the kraits.

The King Cobra or Hamadryad *(Naja hannah)* from eastern India, Burma, Malaya and the Archipelago, South China and the Philippines, feeds on other snakes — though it avoids 'long fanged' vipers. It may attack humans on sight in the mating season, and grows to eighteen feet (largest poisonous snake in the world). It typically rears and spreads its neck-hood when advancing agressively. The colouration is variable.

The Asiatic Cobra *(Naja naja)*, extends from the eastern shores of the Caspian, through India, Ceylon, Burma, Malaya and the Archipelago, Indo-China, Formosa and the Philippines. It rears and spreads a neck hood (typically with spectacle markings) when advancing to attack, and grows to six feet. The colouration is variable.

The beautifully banded primitive Coral-snakes, although possessing lethal venom are reluctant to bite man unless trodden on.

The danger of snake-bite in these areas varies according to a man's occupation, the time of day and the season of the year. For instance, Indian cobras are found particularly in unoccupied dwellings and in fields. Half their recorded bites have therefore occurred during the day, while the rest took place at night when the person bitten was walking in the dark. Kraits, on the other hand, infest occupied houses and the majority of bites take place at night, when an alerted krait comes in contact with a sleeper, for kraits are particularly nocturnal by habit.

There is a tendency for snakes to aestivate in very hot weather, but if this period happens to coincide with the monsoon rains, then they may be encountered when seeking higher and drier quarters than their flooded holes or burrows.

Antivenins for these south Asian snakes are prepared by the Haffkine Institute, Parel, Bombay; the Central Research Institute, Kasauli, and the Institut Pasteur, Paris.

From the hypothetical phylogenetic breeding ground in

tropical Asia, the fixed-fanged neurotoxic-venomed snakes had three possible avenues of dispersion. They could wander northwards through China into Mongolia. This direction however, was unsuitable for the heat loving "cobra" kind and so the species peter out in southern China. Secondly, they could migrate southwards across the then exposed Sakul shelf into Australia (including Tasmania, New Guinea, the Solomon Islands and the Moluccas) which continent they finally overran and were never followed by any other kind of poisonous snake.

There are about five species in Australia which are both dangerous and likely to be encountered by field naturalists; the sixth species is rare, but deadly when confronted:-

The Death 'Adder' (Acanthophis antarcticus), which is found in sandy areas and scrub covered sandstone hills over most of Australia except southern Victoria, has the widest distribution of Australian snakes and also occurs in New Guinea and the Moluccas. Usually it strikes from a coil and holds on. In length it averages two feet. Strangely, it has the appearance of a viper, and its tail ends in a spine which is twitched to attract lizard prey. The death rate of persons bitten is high.

The Australian Brown Snake (Demansia textilis), is distributed widely over Australia in dry areas, scrub, and clay pans, as well as in the wheat and rice fields of Murrumbigee. A variety occurs in New Guinea. It is slender and fast and the most aggressive of Australian snakes, and grows to over six feet, while the venom has especial power of rapid diffusion, which adversely affects treatment.

The Australian Copperhead (Denisonia superba), is the swamp snake of south-east Australia and Tasmania, and is the first snake to appear in spring and the last to hibernate in winter. It is not so aggressive as the brown snake, but six foot specimens are very dangerous.

The Australian Tiger snake (Notechis scutatus), is distributed widely over the drier parts of Australia and Tasmania. This snake is responsible for more fatalities than all the other Australian poison snakes put together. Its venom is the most toxic of any known land snake. Death may occur in one hour after the bite. This snake grows to about six feet and is an aggressive heavy-bodied dark banded snake with a large frontal shield (hence 'scutatus') on the head.

111

The Australian Taipan *(Oxyuranus scutellatus)*, is found in North Australia and New Guinea. It grows to twelve feet and is fortunately not numerous. Very few recoveries from its bite are on record. The dorsal scales are slightly ridged, which distinguishes it from a large specimen of the brown snake, the scales of which are smooth (textile-like).

The Australian Black snake *(Pseudecchis porphyriacus)*, is widespread in Australia. It is a thin fast snake, a good swimmer and is not aggressive unless molested. It is also the commonest of the large Australian poisonous snakes. The Queensland form grows to nine feet, and all the varieties are dangerous in spite of having a venom of lower toxicity than the other highly venomous species.

Antivenins for Australian poison snakes are produced by the Commonwealth Serum Laboratories, Department of Health, Melbourne.

The third possible dispersal route for the "cobra" kind was westwards through the Middle East to the continent of Africa, since they seem to have avoided the presumably cold-winter areas north of the Caspian Sea. The Indian (= Asiatic) Cobra *(Naja naja)*, is still found as far west as Iran, where it is joined by the widely distributed hoodless cobra *(Naja morgani)*, of Iran and Iraq. In Jordan and Israel the 'Egyptian' cobra *(Naja haje)*, occurs, although it is in Africa that this species shows its wide dominance, for it ranges from Morocco, through Algeria, Tunisia and Libya to Egypt and then southwards to Natal, avoiding only the desert centres and areas of high humidity. It grows to six feet in length, is brown in colour, and is nervous and quick to strike. The venom is lethal and typically neurotoxic. The smaller Cape cobra *(Naja nivea)*, overlaps with the 'Egyptian' cobra in South Africa. It is lighter in colour, however, though similarly nervous and resentful.

The Black Cobra *(Naja melanoleuca)*, is, however, the finest of the African cobras. It is limited to the hot humid equatorial forest belt with a southern limit in Rhodesia, and it reaches eight feet in length and is thick and heavy in proportion. Although it is not as nervous as the 'Egyptian' cobra it will attack savagely if cornered. A recognition feature is its shiny black scalation. The venom is lethal.

Africa has two unique 'spitting' snakes, (1) the Blacknecked

Spitting Cobra *(Naja nigricollis)*, of central tropical Africa, which will squirt venom into the eyes from a distance of twelve feet. This fluid must be washed out quickly in order to avoid an acute blinding inflammation. This snake grows to seven feet, and may be surprised in grass or bush, when it will rear and hold its ground. (2) The Ringhals *(Haemachatus haemachatus)*, or Spoegslang of South Africa, which overlaps the territory of the more northern *Naja nigricollis* can easily be differentiated by its keeled (ridged) scales, for all other cobras have smooth scales. It only grows to four feet, and its spitting distance is limited to about six feet, which, however, can still be dangerous to a person peering into rocks or grasses, for like its cousin it always aims for the eyes. These spitting cobras rarely bite humans, and therefore there are few records of systemic poisoning.

There are fish-eating water cobras *(Boulengerina)* in central tropical Africa, the Cameroons, Equatorial Africa, the Congo and Lake Tanganyika, but most specialisation has taken place in the Green and Black Mambas *(Dendroaspis angusticeps)*. These tree cobras are long, thin and speedy, and occur widely in central and southern Africa. They share with the Asiatic Kingcobra a willingness to attack man without provocation during the breeding season, when they become particularly irritable over territorial rights. The green variety reaches eight feet in length, and the black twelve feet. These arboreal cobras have large eyes and very forwardly placed poison fangs. Their venom is typically neurotoxic, and accounts for a considerable percentage of snakebite fatalities in Africa.

Finally, as regards the geographic dispersal of the neurotoxic-venomed snakes, there are the Coral-snakes. Species of these are found in southern Asia, in tropical Africa and in southern North America and northern South America. It can only be suggested that these gaudily coloured, rather primitive, neckless, burrowing-type snakes, which still seek out mainly cold-blooded prey (young snakes and small lizards) found their way to the Americas at a time when Africa was still joined to the South American Continent, and before the larger 'cobra type' had developed sufficiently to colonise so far westwards. These red, white, and yellow-banded little snakes which grow from eighteen inches (North America) to four feet (South America), have an extremely lethal venom, but fortunately do not strike like most 'modern' snakes, although they will turn and bite deliberately if trodden on. Due to their retiring habits and warning colouration recorded bites of humans are rare.

Antivenin for African poisonous snakes is prepared by the Fitz Simons Snake Park Laboratory, Box 1413, Durban, Natal, and also by Behringwerke, Aktiensgesellschaft, Germany.

After the neurotoxic snakes had become established as killers of arthropods, fishes, amphibians and reptiles, new kinds of prey evolved at the end of the age of reptiles. These were small, competitive, fiercely couragious warm-blooded animals — at first part reptile and part mammal. Today, of these early mammals only the spiny anteater *(Tachyglossus aculeatus)* and duck-billed platypus *(Ornithorhynchus anatinus)* survive. They are both found in Australia, and the platypus bears a pair of poison spurs on the hind legs, which should be carefully avoided when handling the living animal.

Some snake species turned to this new source of food and in consequence evolved a new method of killing. Since snake venom is never composed of the same proportions of ingredients in different species, those with a higher proportion of blood toxins or lysins in their venom found they were in a better position for dealing with the new, active and fierce little mammals. Also, those with long fangs could inject this haemotoxic poison more deeply into their prey than snakes with shorter fangs. Long fixed fangs, however, could only be used with the mouth closed, and there is one African genus of small burrowing vipers *(Atractaspis)* which actually so uses its extra long fangs (which however are folded parallel with the lips when not in action), pouring out venom as it strikes. Most long fanged snakes, however, have evolved a method of hinging back these hollow fangs along the upper gums inside the mouth when not in use, and only erect them during the act of striking, when both jaws open at full gape and are almost in line, with the fangs standing out at right angles.

The tips of these fangs are pointed and solid but there is an opening like the eye of a needle just proximal to the tip, through which venom from the hollow fangs is pumped into the tissues of the snake's victim at the instant of penetration.

This large injection of haemotoxic venom quickly shocks warm-blooded prey into submission, so the strike is followed by instant withdrawal and a threatful watch in case the prey tries to escape. This technique is less dangerous to the snake than struggling with a sharp toothed rodent or other mammal. Snakes which adopt this method of killing are known as Vipers (Viperidae) as opposed to the snakes of "Cobra" type (Elapidae).

Probably originating in the tropical 'Indo-China hypothetical phylogenetic breeding grounds', these vipers proved energetic enough to disperse into, and to develop in, Europe, Africa and the Americas (not Australia), leaving behind however, the most dreaded viper of them all, the daboia or Russell's Viper *(Vipera russelli)*, sometimes termed the Ticpolonga ('spotted snake'). This species is distributed through India, Ceylon, Burma, Thailand, Indo-China, Malaya and the Archipelago, including Sumatra, Java, on to Flores (even on Komodo) and southern Yunnan in China. It grows to five feet in length, and warns unwelcome trespassers by hissing loudly with a bellows action of its body. The bite is followed by instant local reaction with haemorrhages (quite unlike the small local reaction to neurotoxic venom). Russell's Viper is one of the most dreaded snakes of the Orient, and joins the Indian cobra and kraits in causing the highest number of deaths in the world due to snake-bite. In accordance with the term 'viper' the young are born viviparously, about thirty at a time. This snake is a rich pale brown with three rows of large black rings down its entire length. It has the typical viperine heavy body, distinct neck, and triangular-shaped head, which is covered with small keeled scales.

These small scales on the top of the head are typical of true vipers, though some few forms still show the ancestral large scales or head plates found on elapine snakes. Fea's Viper *(Azemiops feae)*, found in the Chinese provinces of Szechwan, Kiangsi, and Yunnan is one of these intermediate vipers which resemble the "cobra" type, because of the large head shields.

Along the now semi-desert areas between India and Europe and Africa is found the irritable but small (up to two feet) Sawscaled Viper *(Echis carinata)*. It often lies buried in hot sand with only the head exposed and rubs its scales together to warn off intruders. It is distributed from Ceylon throughout India and westwards to Iran, northwards to Syria, southwards to Aden and then widely throughout Northern Africa. It will jump from its coil in order to strike and is invariably aggressive. Bites from Indian specimens seem to cause only 10–20% mortality, while those from Africa have a much higher death rate. This is presumed to be because African *Echis* are larger, with greater supplies of venom. These vipers are sand coloured with a white mark on the crown resembling the print of a bird's foot.

In northern Africa, Israel, Jordan and Saudi Arabia these saw-scaled vipers are joined by the Eye-horned Sand-viper *(Cerastes cornutus)* and its relatives. It grows to over two feet and causes numerous fatal accidents. The figure-of-eight tracks it makes on sand may be seen in its hunting grounds.

Northwards of Syria, the dangerous *Echis* and *Cerastes* give way to the warmth loving southern relatives of the common northern viper *(Vipera berus)* which latter has a distribution from Scotland (not including Ireland) through Scandinavia and Siberia to Sakhalin Island in the Pacific. This species extends southwards through the temperate zone (for although fond of sunshine it dislikes great heat), until replaced by several sandloving species such as *Vipera aspis,* which is found from Fontainbleau forest to Yugoslavia, and occasionally causes fatalities by its bites, and *Vipera ammodytes,* the long nosed viper of the southern Mediterranean region (not North Africa) including the Balkans, Hungary, Greece, Turkey and Syria, with a northerly range of about 48° north latitude. This snake is considered the most dangerous of the 'European' vipers. There is also the larger blunt-nosed viper *(Vipera lebetina)* which grows to be five feet in length, and is dangerous throughout its wide range from Melos and Cyprus to India, where, due to its colouration, it is sometimes mistaken for a Russell's viper.

In Africa, however, the true vipers come into their own, for apart from the always dangerous though small Saharan sandvipers *Echis* and *Cerastes,* which are paralleled in the dry areas of southern Africa by such small (one foot to eighteen inches long) venomous species as the Berg Adder *(Bitis atropos)* which is found among the plateaus and mountains; the South African Eye-horned Adder *(Bitis cornuta)* of sandy areas where it may be found partly buried in wait for large insects or small rodents and lizards and *Bitis caudalis* (also an eye-horned adder), which prefers the more arid western areas, the heat and good living conditions of Africa south of the Sahara have enabled three 'giant' species of true vipers to evolve, which have no equals among their kind, except the south Asian Russell's Viper.

Firstly, there is the Puff Adder *(Bitis arietans)* which extends over most of the curved plateau that is Africa, avoiding only the desert centres, dense forests and high altitudes. It inhabits sandy grasslands, rocky areas and light forests from southern Morocco to the Cape, as well as southern Arabia. Its form and proportions demonstrate viper development at its peak. This snake is about four and a half feet when fully grown, very thick in section, with a large triangular-shaped head and a very short narrow tail. The hinged curved fangs are of great length, and it strikes so hard from an S loop of the foreparts that it actually jumps during an attack. The action of its venom is usually over in half an hour, and the person bitten either dies in a few days time, or else the portion of the body affected will become gangrenous and slough off at a distinct line of demarcation. Amputation at this stage is often successful. Puff adders hide in ambush beside paths and trails with the head ready to strike, and are probably responsible for the majority of fatal snakebites in Africa. If hungry they hunt by night. The colouration is a pale sandy hue with darker markings.

Secondly, there is the Gaboon Viper *(Bitis gabonica)* which has a more restricted distribution than the puff adder, and is found mainly among the leaves and debris of forest regions through Central Africa. It ranges from Zanzibar to Angola. Like all the big vipers it hisses loudly if it wishes to warn off an intruder. It grows almost to six feet with a girth of about fifteen inches, and its venom is remarkable in containing powerful neurotoxin as well as the typical viperine haemotoxin. It has proportions similar to a puff adder and its rich chevron body-patterns camouflage it completely when it lies among dead leaves.

Thirdly, there is a River Jack or Rhinoceros viper *(Bitis nasicornis).* This inhabits the rain forests of tropical West Africa from Liberia to Kenya. It is semi-aquatic and in spite of the brilliance of its chevroned colouration it is almost impossible to see it on the forest floor. Naturalists, as with all these giant vipers, may very easily tread on a sleeping specimen and receive an immediate strike on the foot or leg. Its venom is more toxic than that of *Bitis gabonica* but a bite from any of these three snakes is most serious.

Finally, of the many remaining African adders, only the Night Adder *(Causus rhombeatus)* is a widespread menace. Its distribution is throughout southern Africa as far north as the Nile. It so consistently lies on warm paths at night that it accounts for the majority of snake bites within its range, as it is frequently stepped on by natives in the dark.

Fortunately, its venom is not highly toxic and the person bitten recovers after a few days of rest. The fangs are comparatively short and appear similar to those of Elapine snakes. It grows to about two and a half feet and is grey with a chain of dark light-edged markings along the back.

Whilst the development of the vipers was taking place in Africa, Europe and Siberia, a new kind of viper appears to have evolved back in the warm south Asian rain-forests. These snakes were viperine in all respects, save that they had a deep 'pit' on either side of the head between the nostril and the eye. These apertures enabled their owners, the 'Pit-Vipers', to sense the presence of warm-blooded animals, and so unerringly to find a rodent in the deepest of forked burrows or a roosting bird on the darkest of nights.

There are two important Asian genera, *Agkistrodon* (with a primitive arrangement of plates or shields on the top of the head), and *Trimeresurus* (with a crown of small unpaired plates or scales). These Asian pit-vipers, like the northern latitude true vipers are somewhat limited in size, their average length being two or three feet.

There are some large species, as for instance *Agkistrodon acutus,* the Crested Adder of China, called the Hundred Pace ("before you die") snake in Formosa, which is heavy bodied, nose-horned and grows to five feet. Although not naturally aggressive this species causes more deaths per bite in Formosa than the local cobra There is also *Trimeresurus flavoviridis,* a 'habu', (and large for its Asian genus) which inhabits the Okinawa and Amami Oshima group of the Ryukyu Islands. It is inclined to be aggressive and grows to six feet, so that its bite is much feared. The mortality of those bitten is about 3%.

It is notable that these small active pit-vipers appear to have migrated east and north, whilst the true vipers travelled west and north. Remains of these hypothetical dispersals occur as species over a very wide area. *Agkistrodon halys* ranges from the

Pescadores to the Yangtze Valley, Japan and north China, where it is found competing with the northern true adders as far west as the Caspian Sea. *Agkistrodon intermedius* has a similar distribution into Mongolia and where it has invaded expedition camps. These *Agkistrodon* are not afraid of climbing mountain ranges, for *Agkistrodon himalayanus*, the Mountain Pit-viper, has been recorded at 16,000 feet, though its altitude preference is five to ten thousand feet. Its range is from Assam along the Himalayas to Kashmir.

Agkistrodon hypnale is found from the hills of Ceylon to the western Ghats, as far north as Bombay, while *Agkistrodon rhodostoma*, the Tropical or Malayan Pit-viper, keeps to the hot Malayan Peninsula and Archipelago, Indo-China, Sumatra and Java.

Trimeresurus, the other genus of Asian pit-vipers, have species with very variant proportions, some being long and slender and others short and stout. They are best known as the "Bamboo snakes and their allies". The terrestrial forms lack prehensile tails and are usually brown or grey with darker markings, while the arboreal kinds have prehensile tails and are often brilliant leaf-green in colour. Fortunately, records of death from their bites are relatively few in spite of their being long fanged and venomous.

Trimeresurus gramineus, the Green (tree) Pit-Viper, is a well known low-jungle species found on the Andamans and Nicobars, and then distributed from Formosa (where it is a main biter) through the Malayan and Indian Orient, avoiding the plains however and keeping to the hills and mountains.

Trimeresurus monticola, the large Spotted Mountain Pitviper, is found along the Himalayas (28,000 feet) from Formosa and Malaya to the hills of Assam and Yunnan, and *Trimeresurus microsquamatus* is the 'Taiwan habu' of Formosa, though also found in the Naga hills and China.

It was the predecessors of these northern pit-vipers which are believed in time past to have found a landbridge across the Bering Straits to the Americas, a journey no true Viper or Elapine (unless the ancestors of the coral-snakes came this way) has ever made for itself.

The poisonous snakes of North and South America are therefore all pit-vipers (except the coral-snakes) and bear a close relationship to the Asiatic *Agkistrodon* and *Trimeresurus.*

The genera of poisonous Pit-vipers of the New World are few. (1) *Agkistrodon* or Moccasins. (2) *Sistrurus* or Dwarf Rattlesnakes (with large plate-scales on the head like *Agkistrodon,* but with a tail-rattle like *Crotalus.* (3) *Crotalus* or Rattlesnakes (found only in North and South America). (4) *Lachesis* (with only one species) the Bushmaster (and related to *Crotalus*). (5) *Bothrops* closely related to the Asian *Trimeresurus,* inclusive of three groups the generalised lance-head pit-vipers, the arboreal 'palm' pit-vipers with prehensile tails, and the terrestrial hog-nosed pit-vipers.

Simplifying the pit-vipers dispersal over North America, it could be said that *Agkistrodon contortrix,* the highland moccasin or 'Copperhead' (which is often divided into a northern and southern species), has occupied the eastern and southern coastal states of the U.S.A. In the north it is found in rocky forested hills where it hibernates in winter, and also in damp tussocky grasslands, for it is fond of frogs, which preference for coldblooded prey, together with the arrangement of plates on the top of its head (instead of the typical small scales of most vipers and pit-vipers) points to a primitive relationship with the Asian pit-vipers. It is not a naturally aggressive snake, but is dangerous to persons clambering among rocks or stepping over fallen trees, as well as those camping in these areas. It grows to three or four feet and vibrates its rattleless tail when disturbed, indicating a relationship with the rattlesnakes, all of which are descended from the same ancestral stock as *Agkistrodon.* It carries a lethal venom, but those bitten do not usually die. The body scales are 'keeled' and due to the depth of its head it is often referred to as the 'Chunkhead'.

The south-eastern United States are also inhabited by another *Agkistrodon,* the Cottonmouth (which opens its mouth before striking, and shows its white gums) or Water Mocassin *(Agkistrodon piscivorus),* which is found along streams, lakes and swamps. It specialises in catching cold-blooded prey, fishes and frogs, even more exclusively than the Copperhead, and also has the generic arrangement of head plates and no tail-rattle. The water mocassin grows to four feet, and is pugnacious when aroused. Its venom is more toxic than that of the Copperhead, but less so than its Central American form *Agkistrodon bilineatus,* the Cantil, which is particularly resentful and venomous.

Related to *Agkistrodon,* (in having head plates and a liking for frogs, though they also eat insects, small rodents and birds), are the two species and subspecies of *Sistrurus,* or 'dwarf rattlesnakes', which rather primitive pit-vipers are found north and south along the chain of the Great Lakes, through north Carolina and Florida to Texas and Mexico. They are remarkable in possessing a tail-rattle which is otherwise only found on the true rattlesnakes. These snakes are small in length, *Sistrurus milarus* (of dry areas) rarely exceeding twenty inches, although *Sistrurus catenatus* (of swampy areas) may reach two to three feet. Their small amount of venom is very toxic, but few fatalities have been reported.

Just as tropical Africa is the preferred home-land of the giant true-vipers, so North America is the preferred environment of the pit-viper rattlesnakes — especially the south western corner including north Mexico. Here, from Canada (about the latitude of Medicine Hat) down into Mexico, and from the Pacific Coast to the Eastern States of the U.S.A. are many species of the genus *Crotalus,* all with the top of the head covered with small scales, and all possessing loose horny segments on their tails, which rattle loudly when vibrated. The Old World vipers give a loud warning hiss when afraid of being trodden on, but the New World rattlesnakes not only hiss but click or buzz their tail violently when man approaches closely, or a ruminant grazes near them.

The numerous species vary in size from *Crotalus willardi,* the tiny Ridge-nosed Rattler of Arizona and Northern Mexico, which grows to fifteen inches, to the Great Eastern Diamond-back Rattler *(Crotalus adamanteus),* which commonly reaches six feet, and occasionally almost nine feet in length. Second in size is the Great Western Diamond-back which may reach seven feet and a weight of fifteen pounds. This snake easily comes first in causing snakebite fatalities in North America, not because its venom is the most toxic, but because of its abundance in numbers and its agility in attack. It is distributed from California to Texas, and often hunts along trails and paths near rocks. Like all true rattlesnakes it prefers warm-blooded prey, principally rodents. It may be found in deserts, where it is of a paler colour than those forms found among rocks or in town garbage dumps (to which it is attracted by the smell of rats).

The commonest of the large rattlesnakes is the Prairie Rattler *(Crotalus viridis)* with its focus in the Great Plains area from eastern Nebraska to the Rockies and southwards to central Mexico. It grows to five feet and persons bitten have a recorded death rate of 7%.

There are two other North America rattlesnakes of particular note. Firstly, the Timber Rattler *(Crotalus horridus)*, which has an eastwards distribution from where the Prairie Rattler becomes scarce, and a north and south extension from Maine to Florida. In the winter time it hibernates in deep rock fissures (often in company with water moccasins). There are hill types and swamp-moss types. It may grow to six feet, but there are surprisingly few fatalities recorded, considering the quantity of lethal venom it can expend at a bite. Secondly, the Horned Rattler or Sidewinder *(Crotalus cerastes)* is a small sandcoloured desert species found in southern California, Nevada, Arizona and Southwest Utah. A large scale over each eye forms an upright eye-horn. The snake moves over the sand by looping the body laterally after the manner of the African *Cerastes* and *Bitis* sand-adders. Its bite rarely causes death.

Antivenins for North American poisonous snakes are prepared by the Wyeth Laboratories, Philadelphia I, Pa., U.S.A.

In Central America, the type of country preferred by rattlesnakes gives way to hot humid forests dominated by two different genera of snakes, although one species of tropical rattlesnake, the Casabel *(Crotalus durissus terrificus),* has firmly established itself in South America. This is the only rattler found east of the Andes, and ranges south of the humid Amazon basin to northern Argentina (avoiding only the Grand Chaco). It overlaps with *Crotalus durissus,* the Tropical Mexican Rattlesnake, in the north western corner of South America, where this species has infiltrated into the subcontinent from the north.

There are several varieties of *Crotalus durissus terrificus* with some differences in their poison. The typical form is remarkable for having largely neurotoxic venom, which contributes to this snake being considered the most poisonous of all rattlers. Humans bitten by the casabel tend to loose control of their neck muscles, hence the saying that "this snake always breaks a man's neck".

The first of these genera is *Lachesis,* with but one species closely allied to the rattlesnakes. This is *Lachesis muta* the Bushmaster, which is distributed through southern tropical Central America and tropical South America, where it occurs in humid forests and riverine areas. It is probably most numerous in Costa Rica and Panama and is greatly feared in Tobago and Trinidad. It grows to twelve feet, which makes it the world's largest viper. It hunts warm-blooded prey by day or night, and is able to sidewind over sand. It is fearless and aggressive, a characteristic found in many South American poisonous snakes, and will actively follow humans if irritated. It has great fang length (up to one and a half inches) with copious supplies of poison. Though rattleless it may warn by rapidly vibrating the end of the tail, or it may attack silently *(= muta).* Fortunately, it is nowhere abundant. It is against this snake, and indeed most other rodent-eating poisonous snakes, that campers in the open are advised to clear away all undergrowth from around the site. If this material is burnt to form a guardian perimeter, so much the better. The ashes will discourage foraging ants, spiders, centipedes, scorpions, and in particular rodents, for it is the scent of these little animals that attracts snakes into camps, food-stores, villages, and refuse-dumps.

The second genus , *Bothrops,* contain very many species, which are believed to be the modern descendants of the migrant ancestors of *Trimeresurus.* Here, in the humid tropical forests of Central and South America this genus seems to have evolved every variation of ground and arboreal poisonous snake. They may all be differentiated from *Agkistrodon* by having small scales on the top of the head.

The most dreaded of these Central and South American *Bothrops* is the Fer-de-lance *(Bothrops atrox),* which also occurs in the West Indian islands of St. Lucia, Martinique, Tobago and Trinidad. It grows to over eight feet and usually hunts by night, lying coiled by day ready to strike. It can swim and cover ground swiftly, and is very vicious when angry. The venom is powerfully haemotoxic, destroying the red cells and blood vessels, and causing bleeding from the eyes, mouth and kidneys. These snakes are greatly attracted to rats and mice in garbage heaps.

123

Of the three dozen or so remaining *Bothrops* species, the socalled 'palm vipers' are perhaps the most important to the field naturalist, for they have the habit of coiling around low branches along jungle trails and may easily bite at head level if disturbed. *Bothrops schlegeli,* the Bocaraca, is an example of these colourcamouflaged dangerous tree pit-vipers.

There are several *Bothrops* species *(e.g. Bothrops jararacusau)* known locally by such names as 'jararaca' and 'urutu'. These are of fer-de-lance type and dominate the Central and South American jungles as efficiently as rattlesnakes do the plains of North America. They are all large snakes with lethal venom and an excessive length of fangs, which together with their vindictive quickness, makes them very dangerous to persons exploring their territories.

The Jumping Viper or Timba of Mexico and Central America is capable of striking from a coil-spring for up to a yard distant. Its fangs, fortunately, in spite of its large head, are comparatively short and its venom is less toxic than most *Bothrops.* It is related to the ground frequenting 'Hognosed' Pit-vipers, which all strike so hard that they jump forward. *Bothrops lansbergi* is an example of a hognosed viper, and like many *Bothrops* will vibrate its rattleless tail as a warning. A full bite from these somewhat small snakes can however be very dangerous and they range from arid environments to humid forests.

Antivenins against Central and South American poisonous snakes are prepared by the Institute Butantan, Caixa Postal 65, Sao Paulo, Brazil, and by the Institute Pinheiros, Rua Teodoro Sampaio, 1860, Sao Paulo, Brazil.

The foregoing geographical distribution of dangerous snakes is intended to remove some of the complications caused by the presentation of many different species separated from adequate descriptions. Since there are five books enabling an explorer easily to identify the snakes of the world, he can but study the principles of the subject and then correspond with such institutions as the British Museum of Natural History, who will help him with the finer points of identification.

A number of poisonous snakes of little practical importance has been omitted from this chapter. Examples are the rearfanged whiplike Boomslang *(Dispholidus typus)* of Africa, which bites man rarely, though it carries a very toxic venom; and the seasnakes (Hydropinae), which are found in the warm seas stretching from the Persian Gulf to the Far East, with one species *(Pelamis platurus)* in western American waters, because, although extremely venomous (neutrotoxic, since they are related to the 'cobras') they very seldom bite man, perhaps because their mouths are formed to catch fish rather than to defend themselves against mammals. Finally, it is interesting to remember that there are no poisonous snakes in Ireland, Madagascar, New Zealand, Hawaiian Islands, Norfolk Islands, most Pacific Islands, Cuba, Jamaica, Haiti and Porto Rico, and the small West Indian Islands.

SUBJECT INDEX

(page numbers in italics refer to
unfigured drawings)

The Collected Letters
of a Nobody

Also by Keith Waterhouse

The Collected Letters of a Nobody
Including Mr Pooter's Advice to his Son

KEITH WATERHOUSE

Illustrated by John Jensen

MICHAEL JOSEPH
LONDON

First published in Great Britain by Michael Joseph Ltd
44 Bedford Square, London WC1
1986

Waterhouse, Keith
    The Collected letters of a nobody (including
    Mr Pooter's advice to his son).
    I. Title
    823'.914[F]   PR6073.A82

    ISBN 0 7181 2549 5

Typeset in Sabon
by Cambrian Typesetters
Printed and bound in Great Britain
by Billing & Sons Ltd, Worcester

CONTENTS

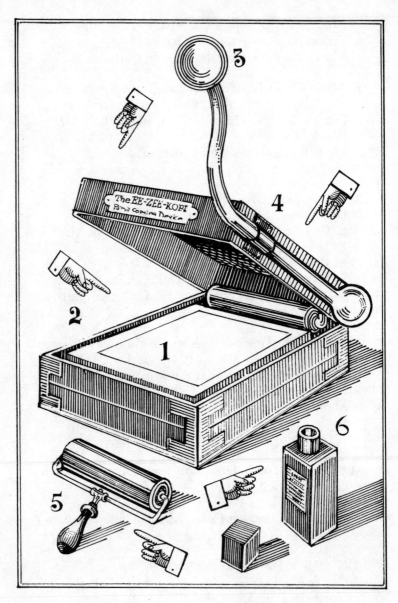

The Eee-zee-kopi Patent Copying Device

INTRODUCTION

On Lady Day 1888, one Charles Pooter, quite a senior clerk with the stockbroking firm of Perkupp & Co., took up residence with his wife Caroline at 'The Laurels,' Brickfield Terrace, Holloway, North London, a rented house backing on to the railway.

Concurrent with the move, Pooter appears to have been smitten by intimations of immortality. At any rate he commenced to keep a diary, with hopes of publication.

He began at the same time to keep copies of all the letters he wrote, presumably with the same aspiration of their one day being collected and appearing in book form. This was very much in line with the literary fashion of the period. As *Punch* noted, 'Everybody who is anybody is publishing reminiscences, diaries, notes, autobiographies and recollections.' Pooter would have seen no reason why the private papers of a suburban clerk should have recommended themselves any less to the reader than those of any political time-server or retired field-marshal.

The Diary Of A Nobody, as we know, eventually did find a publisher. It is from its pages thus made public that we first find evidence not only that Charles Pooter was a prodigious correspondent, even by Victorian standards, but that he was consciously – self-consciously, even – composing at least some of his letters for posterity. The two dozen he explicitly makes mention of having written (there are many other entries – supper or meat tea invitations requiring an acknowledgement, to take an obvious example – where it is implicit that Pooter would have put pen to paper) are the subject of many a self-congratulatory word from their initiator – he has written a 'very satirical' letter to Merton, a wine merchant (April 24 '88), a 'determined' letter to Burwin-Fosselton of the Holloway Comedians (Nov 25 '88), a 'very satirical' note to Mrs Lupkin, a Southend landlady (April 23 '89), 'sixteen pages, closely written' to Mr

9

Crowbillon, a former client of Perkupp & Co. (May 14 '89), and so on.

Quoting a line from an aggrieved letter to his friend Cummings (April 17 '88) Pooter notes: 'I have copied this verbatim in the diary, because I think it is one of the most perfect and thoughtful sentences I have ever written.' Yet apart from that one short extract, and the reproduction almost in full of a brief missive to the laundress (May 31 '89) with which he pronounces himself 'rather pleased . . . for I thought it very satirical,' nowhere else in his diary does Pooter make any effort to impress upon the potential reader, by verbatim or summarised example, his proficiency as a correspondent. It was this uncharacteristic omission which convinced Pooter scholars that copies of at least the more significant letters – certainly the 'very satirical' ones – must have been preserved elsewhere. And so it proved.

The search began and ended in the loft of 'The Laurels,' long derelict but now happily awaiting conversion to the standards of what, after a period of neglect and degeneration, has reverted to a fashionable neighbourhood for the middle classes, though of a higher echelon than in the Pooters' day. There, wedged behind the cold water cistern and overlooked for three-quarters of a century or more, was discovered a battered and cobweb-covered japanned tin trunk labelled 'Effects of Chas Pooter Esq Decd' and addressed to Messrs Hudson's Ecosevephoron at Victoria, where, so the depository's old ledgers show, the Pooters' household possessions were stored following Charles' death in 1908 (Carrie had predeceased him by a year), against the day when after a suitable period of mourning, their only son Lupin, who had a horror of all things Victorian, could decently send the entire contents of 'The Laurels' for auction. Had the loft been cleared more diligently, we may be sure that the Pooter Letters would have been sold as butter paper.

At first sight the contents of the trunk proved disappointing, appearing as they did to consist only of an accumulation of mouldering receipts, newspaper cuttings of no discernible significance, railway timetables, cheap almanacs and back numbers of *Pearson's Weekly*. Beneath this detritus, however, and carefully separated from it by a folded copy of the *Daily*

Mail commemorative issue for Queen Victoria's Diamond Jubilee, was the cache of Pooter papers – all that are known to exist, and comprising:

1. The two Letts' scribbling diaries for 1888–89 which with all their omissions (563 dates out of the two years are left blank) and excisions (the entries between August 30 and October 29 '88 having been ripped out and used to wrap up kitchen fat and leavings by Mrs Birrel or Birrell, the Pooters' charwoman) make up *The Diary Of A Nobody* as we know it. Published during the diarist's lifetime, the original would have been copied and returned to him.

2. The slim bundle of schoolroom composition books in which Carrie Pooter, in a spirit of affectionately (on the whole) malevolent retaliation, kept her own secret diary. Poignantly tipped into the last of these volumes is Carrie's death certificate recording her demise of Stanks's Disease at the age of sixty-four and seven months; it is safe to assume by the very fact of the diary's continued existence, given the abrasive nature of some of the home truths it contains, that not until his wife's death did Charles Pooter learn that she had all along been keeping a journal paralleling his. Edited by the compiler of the present volume, the manuscript was published as *Mrs Pooter's Diary* in 1983.

3. Three manilla folders containing facsimiles of holograph letters penned by Charles Pooter between April 1888 and July 1889 – the exact span of his intermittently-kept diary. We may make of the coincidence what we will: Pooter's decision to discontinue the *Diary* may have precipitated a similar falling away of interest in the somewhat laborious routine of pressing out copies of all his correspondence; or the difficulties he was experiencing in continuing to produce copies by the process he had been using (see July 10 '89: To Messrs Reprograph Ltd (successors to the Ee-zee-kopi Co. Ltd)) could have drained what enthusiasm remained – it was always spasmodic – for the associated ritual of keeping a diary. Or perhaps he had simply lost interest in immortalising himself any longer and had taken up some other interest such as varnishing (see July 4 '89: To Messrs R. & R. Cargle, Oilmen).

The three folders are labelled respectively, '1888,' '1889' and 'Letters To My Son' – this in underscored Gothic lettering with illuminated initials (further proof that the collection was meant for a wider audience than that embraced by 'The Laurels'). This outstanding example of calligraphy – one of Pooter's hobbies – is marred by a scrawled pencil graffito in another hand, almost certainly that of Lupin, 'What sauce!!!'

The letters in their discovered state showed signs of considerable disturbance, being carelessly stuffed into the three folders willy-nilly and without regard to chronology or category. Many of them were torn or crumpled, some disfigured by footprints or food stains, others adrift from their continuation sheets which might be in another file or missing altogether. Some of the torn sheets have been folded and deliberately ripped in two, probably for use as spills. Allowing even of these mutilations, the collection is certainly still far from complete. Of the sixteen-page letter to Mr Crowbillon, for instance, only one page survives. There is no trace of 'an affectionate note' which Pooter records in the *Diary* (July 31 '88) as leaving on Carrie's dressing table with a present of a bangle. The earliest of the extant 'Letters To My Son' (May 1 '88) calls Lupin to task for failing to explain a theatrical magazine discovered under his mattress during the move to 'The Laurels.' Clearly there must have existed a previous letter in which such an explanation was originally called for. Equally clearly, it must have been abstracted from the file by Lupin, since it exists no longer. Probably other 'Letters To My Son' too personally embarrassing for their recipient may have been removed by the same hand – there are some otherwise inexplicable gaps in what was overall a regular if one-sided correspondence.

Lupin's covert censorship apart, the deficiencies and depredations of the Pooter Letters may safely be laid at the door of the incorrigible Mrs Birrell, given her record with other archive material. Where the papers were housed between July 1889 and Pooter's death we are not to know, but it was most probably – at Carrie's insistence, since storage space at 'The Laurels' was at a premium – on a shelf in the cellar. This would account not only for some of them having been gnawed by rats and the otherwise inexplicable coal mark on a note to Mr Perkupp (November 13 '88) but for the generally sorry state in which the whole collection was found. We may surmise that the charwoman, in reaching down some object from an upper shelf (probably a gin bottle) inadvertently knocked the three folders to the cellar flags, spilling their contents. In her slatternly way she would have scooped up the scattered documents and crammed them back into the folders as offhandedly as she would have stuffed feathers back into a cushion, thereafter, having ignorantly identified the smudgy facsimiles as so much waste paper cluttering up the cellar (Mrs Birrell was unlikely to have been more than barely literate, if that), regarding them as on a level with scullery rags.

Of the 241 surviving Pooter Letters not thus relegated to cleaning pewter, lining knife-boxes or lighting fires, 168 have been selected for publication in this volume. The omissions are the merely routine – invitations to meat tea, notes sent round with forgotten umbrellas etc., where these are unadorned with any observation or embellishment that would characterise them as unmistakeably the work of Charles Pooter; the repetitious – i.e., the near-identical letters to that of August 11 '88 to the chief clerk of Fripps, James & Co., stockbrokers, supplicating employment for Lupin, which Pooter unsuccessfully despatched to other business houses in the City; and the illegible – those too faint or too blotchy to be read owing to Pooter's inexpertise with the Ee-zee-kopi machine, and those such as the letter to an unknown correspondent (date obliterated) inexplicably returned to its folder after apparently being used for blackleading the grate.

Where Pooter, an inveterate if unpublished writer of 'Letters to the Editor,' penned different versions on the same theme to several newspapers, only one version has been used. Where several drafts exist – there are, for example, no fewer than twenty-nine facsimile acceptances of one single invitation to the Mansion House Ball, each varying from its fellows by but a word or punctuation mark – only the one judged to be the final version has been included. Where the original letter rather than a copy has been filed, it has been taken that Pooter must have changed his mind about posting it, and such has been indicated in the text.

Not only the 'Letters To My Son' but the entire Pooter correspondence, as it survives, is one-sided. A compulsive hoarder, Charles Pooter would unquestionably have meticulously kept both every reply to his letters (save the one or two torn into little pieces in rage) and those letters from others requiring or provoking replies from him. All that remains of them are the handful quoted in the *Diary*. It seems likely that when the Pooter papers came to be packed for storage, his files of incoming letters would have been put away in a separate box from that containing the copies of his outgoing ones, perhaps together with other vanished documents such as Mrs Pooter's postcards from her sojourns with her friend Mrs James, of Sutton, Pooter's 'cheap address-book,' and the port-stained Mansion House Ball invitation, all of which are specifically mentioned in the *Diary*. If such was the case and they fell into Lupin's hands as personal effects worthless at auction, we may be sure that with his contempt for memorabilia he would have had even scanter regard for their safekeeping than would that vandal of 'The Laurels,' Mrs Birrell.

K.W.

14

APRIL 1888

To:

*Mr Borset, Butterman – Excelsior Fire, Flood & Accident
Assurance Co. – Elastic Aids For The Poor Society –
Mr James, of Sutton – 'Answers To Correspondents,'*
Gardeners' Referee & Athenaeum – *L. Cummings Esq. –
R. Gowing Esq. – D.P. Merton Esq., Wines & Spirits –
Pinkford's, Paint Mfrs & Artists' Sundrymen.*

APRIL 1888

Considering the thousand and one arrangements that would have had to be made without recourse to the telephone and when the sixpenny telegram, for an ordinary suburban couple, was a luxury only to be indulged in as a last resort, the Pooters' correspondence bridging the removal to Holloway from their 'dear little house' in Shanks Place, Peckham, must have been heavy.

Clues to the sheer volume of it are to be found in Charles Pooter's scribbling diary (which he was yet to commence as a diary proper) where a ticked list of names indicates that at least nine change-of-address cards were sent out during this period. There are also, in the margins of a lengthy inventory of the Pooters' household effects occupying twelve and a half pages of the diary, numerous memoranda concerning letters or postcards to be written:

Mem. Write piano tuner.

Mem. Sumpter [a fellow-sidesman at the Metropolitan Tabernacle] to retn *Cassell's Book Of In-door Amusements* by Wed latest, if not too much trouble after 6 mths.

Mrs James, of Sutton. Do., *Common Diseases Of Women*, but to be posted to Holloway *after* Wed. [In view of the volume's delicate subject matter, and the fact that Mrs James was her oldest friend, it seems likely that this reminder would have been written by Carrie.]

Mem. Retn next door's *Scopeley's Cosmographic Atlas* with apols for oversight.

Mem. Enquire of Messrs Carter Patterson whether they will pack coal.

Mem. Write Mr Perkupp re: ½ day off.

Further annotations, in the same red ink used to tick off each item on the inventory to confirm its safe arrival at 'The

Laurels,' indicate correspondence entered into *post* the removal:

> *Mem.* Write Stainbank [the landlord's agent] re: gravy odour and fungoid growth in pantry.
> *Mem.* Write Messrs Carter Patterson re: missing hatbox containing Gossware. [The Gossware evidently turned up. See April 6 '88: To Excelsior Fire, Flood & Accident Assurance Co.]
> *Mem.* Write W[illie] [their son Lupin, later to abandon his Christian name in favour of his mother's maiden name] re: periodical under mattress.
> *Mem.* Write stiff note to James, of Sutton, re: observations in his wife's hand in margins of *Common Diseases Of Women.*

In addition to these memoranda, there is a two-page list of 'Things To Be Done' – though whether in writing or verbally is not always clear. 'Advertise mangle' – 'Pay up Sheldon [an odd-job man]' – 'Gd character for Mrs F[elt] [the cleaning woman at Shanks Place]' – 'Retrieve travelling clock from mender's' – 'Advise C[ummings] & G[owing] [friends in Holloway] of arrival date' – 'Send announcement to "Notes fm Clocktower," *Peckham Free Advertiser* re: regrettable departure fm district of well-known, respected &c &c residents Mr & Mrs C. Pooter.' (Presumably the news failed to create a stir in the editorial sanctum, since this item is scrawled over with the addendum: 'Personal col ¼d per 3 words. So much for "Free" *Advertiser*!!!')

More lengthily, there are notes for a missive which Pooter clearly looked forward to composing: 'Send one of my satirical letters to Universal Pantechnicon Coy re: preposterous estimate – almost double that of Messrs Carter Patterson – perhaps misunderstanding – do not wish to buy van & horses, merely to hire same – or is handwriting at fault & firm has mistaken *Holloway* for *Holyhead*! – apols for wasting *valuable*(!) time.' This scrappy précis is all that exists of the Pooter Letters covering the transition from Peckham to Holloway – as well as, for that matter, all the years before it.

The 'Things To Be Done' catalogue, meticulously crossed through with ruled lines as each task was accomplished, is mainly concerned with the minutiae of settling in at 'The Laurels.' The last item, however, is significantly unconnected with these domestic preoccupations. It reads: 'Reply *Exchange & Mart* advt re: Ee-zee-kopi.'

An Ee-zee-kopi patent copying device – 'Hardly used, 40/– when new, 25/– COD for quick sale, inc roller, papers, ink & gelatine' – was advertised in the *Exchange & Mart* dated March 30, when the Pooters had been but three days in their new home. The accounts in the back of Pooter's scribbling diary show that he drew a sum in that amount from the Economic Small Savings Bank, Cannon Street, on April 3, the same day that he commenced the *Diary*.

We do not know precisely when the second-hand Ee-zee-kopi machine was delivered. The transaction is not mentioned in the *Diary* – perhaps Pooter, fearing Carrie's wrath at his extravagance, secretly installed his copying paraphernalia in the cellar, like some printer of seditious pamphlets, and refrained from confiding in his diary in case his wife was covertly reading it (she was).

At all events, we can be certain that it was on April 6 1888, that Charles Pooter, after a day or so's unsatisfactory experiments with the Ee-zee-kopi (some of these totally indecipherable efforts survive, their reverse side having been used for making copy letters when he was more at home with the machine; the special paper provided being practically transparent, however, these later examples are illegible too) achieved the first blurred and badly-aligned facsimile that is the earliest of the Pooter Letters. A postcard (undated, but see the *Diary* entry for April 6: 'Eggs for breakfast simply shocking . . . sent them back to Borset with my compliments, and he needn't call any more for orders'), it was despatched by hand to a local tradesman:

To Mr BORSET, Butterman,
9 Sharnforth Place, N
Mr Borset – If the eggs you sent round yesterday are fresh, then I am a Dutchman! Pray strike the 1/– charged for them from your account, render same immediately, & do *not* trouble yourself to call again for orders.
C. Pooter

The Ee-zee-kopi, a simplified domestic version of the 'jellygraph' duplicating apparatus then common in offices and institutions, was but one of a dozen or so patent copying machines which Pooter would have seen advertised – the Autocopyist, the Amateur Lithographer, the Presto! Copy Press and so on, generally priced at between three and four guineas. At forty shillings – and considering the regularity with which 'hardly used' and 'as new' models were advertised in the *Exchange & Mart* – the Ee-zee-kopi is unlikely to have been the best of the bunch.

According to a summary of the 'Instructions for use' in an illustrated half-page advertisement in *Whitaker's Almanack* for 1887 ('Invaluable to Clergymen & Business Men'), the Ee-zee-kopi was 'the simplest apparatus for reproducing to be found.' 'A perfect fac-simile' of a holograph manuscript could be obtained by laying the page on a bed of gelatine and applying pressure with a hinged spring-lid, thus creating an impression which, after the gelatine had been coated with an oil-based heliotrope ink, could be transferred to sheets of specially-supplied porous tissue paper by the same pressurising process, the disturbed gelatine surface then being cleared by gentle application of a hand-roller lined with blotting paper.

It seems a messy and cumbersome operation but Pooter appears quickly to have mastered it, for following the flawed triumph of that pioneering postcard to Mr Borset on April 6, facsimiles of Pooter letters positively poured out of the Ee-zee-kopi machine – one to an insurance company that same day, and at least four more during the ensuing week:

To EXCELSIOR FIRE, FLOOD & ACCIDENT
ASSURANCE CO. LTD,
Excelsior Bldgs, Lothbury, Bank, EC

Sirs –   April 6 '88
In respect of the 'All Risks' (except Snow Damage) Policy taken out with your esteemed Company on my behalf by Messrs Carter Patterson, to cover the removal of my effects from Shanks Place, Peckham, SE, to the above address, I wish to claim for damage caused to the following items, viz:–

Item: Bad hair-crack in Gossware pie-funnel bearing Broadstairs coat-of-arms. Replacement cost when next at Broadstairs (August), 3d.

Item: *Bees & Beekeeping* Vol. II (*Practical Management of the Hive*) – back cover ripped off. Rebinding cost of both vols (as otherwise would not match): at estimate, 2/2d.

Item: Banjo (property of my son) dented, skin torn, two strings snapped and plectrum missing. Write-off, but as was acquired second-hand in exchange for lawn tennis racquet, would accept 7/6d.

Item: Splintered peg on umbrella stand. New peg at cost, 2d.

Item: Priceless antiquity, prob. Roman – a terra-cotta drinking vessel passed down through three generations. Reduced to smithereens. Say 1 gn.

The above damaged objects are available for inspection by your Assessor at any reasonable hour; otherwise an early settlement in the amount of £1 11s 1d (grand total) would oblige.

I am, &c &c,
C. Pooter

To THE SECRETARY, ELASTIC AIDS
FOR THE POOR SOCIETY,
Finsbury Pavement, EC

My dear Sir,   April 7 '88

Thank you most warmly for your cordial circular letter welcoming us to Holloway, wherein you solicit a subscription or donation to the Society.

While comprehending that Institution's sore need of funds in continuing its good work, unfortunately my *own* funds are not without their limits, and I am already hard-pressed by virtue of having the privilege to be an Annual Half-guinea Subscriber to the Freshfields Asylum For Idiots And Imbeciles near Reading, where my wife has strong family connections.

Such being the position, I must regretfully decline the honour of availing myself of your kind invitation.

I remain, my dear Sir, yours &c &c,

C^{has} Pooter

PS My wife's connections are with the town of Reading, not with the Asylum.

To B. JAMES Esq.,

'Latakia,' School Lane,

Sutton, Surrey

My dear James,   April 8 '88

Will you accept my assurances, as a gentleman, that nothing was farther from my mind than to suggest – I am not so lacking in breeding!! – that you call your good lady to order for her – I have said 'facetious,' you would prefer 'harmlessly jocular,' and I most readily accept the amendment – marginalia to *Common Diseases Of Women*. My purpose in drawing this to your attention was merely to remark, in the most general way, that inasmuch as the annotation of books with pencilled comments is a question of taste – I do not say *good* taste or *bad* taste, I say *taste* – my *personal* inclination, so far as my own small library is concerned, is to allow the author the last word in his own work!

Having no wish to fall out over such a trifle, I beg that we now consider the subject closed. By the bye, I see no reason why our 'other halves' should be troubled with knowledge of this small misunderstanding. Once again, looking forward to welcoming Mrs James and your good self to 'The Laurels,'

Believe me, Most cordially yours,

Charles Pooter

To T. STALLARD Esq., Small Claims Manager,

Excelsior Fire, Flood & Accident Assurance Co. Ltd

Dear Sir,   April 8 '88

I am in receipt of your communication of yesterday's date. Let it be said at once that whilst my claim may be 'small' to the Excelsior &c &c Company, £1 11s 1d is no mean sum to one of average means such as the undersigned.

To deal with the specific enquiries brought up in your – if I may so – quibbling reply:–

1. I cannot agree that there is any discrepancy between the adjective 'bad' and the adjectival use of 'hair' to describe the crack suffered by the Gossware pie-funnel; nor is it germane whether the article was purchased for utilitarian or ornamental use. If utilitarian, then it may well have been so structurally weakened by the crack that the heat of the kitchen range might easily cause its utter disintegration (in which contingency a 'small' claim for a pie, as well as for a pie-funnel, would lie). If ornamental – as is the case, the pie-funnel being part of my wife's considerable collection of Gossware 'trifles' from this or that resort – then any crack, hair-line or no, must be aesthetically deleterious. I must therefore insist on re-imbursement in full of the replacement cost of 3d.

2. As a fair man I concede that Vol. II of *Bees & Beekeeping* might be re-bound in as similar a cloth to that of Vol. I as to make no difference. Notwithstanding your gratuitous deprecation of my library – 'the same cheap binding' – I am prepared to reduce this claim to 1/1d.

3. My sole purpose in stressing that the damaged banjo was the property of my son was to disabuse the Excelsior of any impression that this claim emanated from a person of frivolous disposition who is given to strumming cakewalks. I certainly did not anticipate entering into a pedantic argument as to whether my son's personal belongings are covered by a policy on his parents' household effects. Should you wish to stick to the letter, rather than the spirit, of our contract, however, allow me to point out that the tennis racquet for which the banjo was exchanged, was brought into the house by myself, and was not, strictly speaking, my son's to dispose of. This, I fancy, makes the banjo my property. That being said, I will concur with your surmisal that my son has outgrown his interest in the instrument, though not with your conjecture that it would have ended its days in the lumber room. Unquestionably, when next home on holiday and 'short of

the ready' as young men chronically are, he would have disposed of the banjo for cash, realising, so my information has it, perhaps five shillings. In all the circumstances, I am happy to adjust my claim to such a sum.

4. I am not prepared to haggle, Sir, over a twopenny hat-peg. It may well be that hat-pegs may be bought for 9d a half dozen. I have no use for half a dozen hat-pegs. My need is for one (1) hat-peg, the price quoted for which by Messrs Farmerson, ironmongers – address furnished if so desired – is 2d. I reject out of hand your cheeseparing *pro rata* offer of 1½d.

5. I am unable to put a precise valuation upon the terra-cotta drinking vessel, since to the best of my knowledge it has never been valued. My wife once took it to the Sir Frank Napper Museum in Camberwell, where the door-keeper was offhand in his manner. If you assure me that in the absence of any evidence as to the object's antiquity, you are empowered to authorise payment only up to the intrinsic value of the terra-cotta, then so be it, but I should not lightly accept less than four shillings.

Trusting that the above explanations are to your satisfaction, I now look forward to an expeditious conclusion to this transaction, and to receiving settlement in full of the sum of 10/6d (grand total as adjusted) without further ado.

I am, &c &c,
C. Pooter

To THE EDITOR,
Gardeners' Referee & Athenaeum,
Bellows Court, Fleet Street, EC

Attⁿ 'Answers to Correspondents' Dept –

Sir – April 8 '88
My garden runs down to the railway. Are there any salad vegetables which, more than others, thrive upon steam? The garden is north-facing.

I am, &c &c,
'PRUNER,' Holloway (C. Pooter)

[So far as is known, 'Pruner's enquiry was never answered. As luck would have it, *Gardeners' Referee & Athenaeum* was within a fortnight of amalgamating with *Christian Gardener*, when its 'Answers To Correspondents' backlog would have been quietly jettisoned.]

After this initial burst of industry, Pooter appears to have laid aside his pen for a while. At least there are no records of any correspondence for the next eight days. Then, however, he was to be provoked into an angry bout of letter-writing.

The *Diary* for Sunday April 15 documents a painful episode involving Pooter's friends Cummings and Gowing and one Stillbrook, who carried him off to Hampstead where, claiming to be 'bona fide travellers' (as the Sabbath licensing laws then required them to be) from Blackheath, they gained access to a public house, leaving Pooter, who had naively admitted coming from nearby Holloway, fuming outside for 'the best part of an hour.' The following evening, still vexed, he wrote to Cummings:

To L^{eo.} CUMMINGS Esq.,
'Longshanks,' Brickfield Terrace,
Holloway, N

My dear Cummings,   April 16 '88
    I believe it must have escaped my mind to mention to you and Gowing that our doorbell still awaits repair, so that it is necessary for callers to knock quite loudly in order to make their presence known. If my old friends came round last evening to offer an explanation for their thoughtless and wounding conduct on our walk to Hampstead in the afternoon, and were left standing on the doorstep in consequence of not being heard, then I am truly sorry. (I should be even sorrier to learn that they had not troubled themselves to call at all!)
    Believe me, my dear Cummings, Yours sincerely,
C. Pooter

The letter was not sent. Across the top, before filing it away in his as yet slim folder of facsimile copies, Pooter noted:

Leaving Pooter fuming outside

26

'Wrote in same vein to Gowing but had second thoughts.' But second thoughts led only to third thoughts. The next day, still brooding, though in a more conciliatory frame of mind, Pooter wrote:

> To R^{chd} GOWING Esq., c/o Mr Mendelssohn,
> 19 Hospital Road, Holloway, N
>
> My dear Gowing,   April 17 '88
>   I hope you and our old friend Cummings (I shall be dropping him a line in similar terms) will not take it amiss if I offer you a friendly word of warning concerning your friend Mr Stillbrook. Whilst it is always a pleasure to make the acquaintance of any friend of ——

There the letter breaks off. Perhaps Pooter, a fastidious stylist, was dissatisfied with the repetition of 'friend' four times in as many lines. That he began afresh and this time completed it is certain, for the *Diary* records: '. . . Afterwards, tore up the letter and determined not to *write* at all, but to *speak* quietly to them.' Why Pooter chose to retain this opening fragment while destroying the final draft is a mystery. Most likely it was filed away in error.

His forbearance in refraining from posting either the satirical letter of the 16th or his 'kind little note' of the following day earned no plaudits from his friends. On the contrary: the *Diary* (April 17) relates how 'dumbfounded' Pooter was at receiving a sharp letter from Cummings, reproving him for his high dudgeon on the walk back from Hampstead.

Pooter's studied reply must have been a classic. Unfortunately it is lost to us, having doubtless fallen prey to Mrs Birrell. One sentence of it, however, remains for posterity, for it was this which Pooter copied into his diary as 'one of the most perfect and thoughtful sentences I have ever written': 'I thought I was the aggrieved party; but as I freely forgive you, you – feeling yourself aggrieved – should bestow forgiveness on me.'

The episode thus brought to a conclusion (albeit not a satisfactory one, since Cummings and Gowing were left with the impression that he had apologised), Pooter next turned

27

his acerbic pen to a cousin of Cummings, one Merton, a wine and spirits merchant. The exchange began congenially enough:

To D.P. MERTON Esq.,
Messrs Merton & Spock, Vintners,
Lower Ground Floor, 196 Handiman Lane, E

Dear Mr Merton, April 20 '88

This is to confirm my order of 1 doz. of your 'Lockanbar' whisky @ 36/– nett.

In the course of our agreeable conversation last evening, you were good enough to intimate that should we ever want passes for the theatre, we need but to say the word. I hope you will not think me forward in availing myself of this kind invitation and requesting four (4) passes for next Monday, when we have friends coming up from Sutton to stay with us.

Our preference would be, in the order named, for the Opera at Covent Garden, the revival of *The Mikado* with Mr Geo Grossmith, *Guy Faraday's Past* at the Haymarket, or *Her Mentor* at the Lyceum. Failing which, and always provided that the piece be not in French, we commend ourselves to that good taste which so much evidenced itself when Cummings did us the honour of bringing you to our house.

I shall be very much obliged to you, my dear Mr Merton, for this favour, which again I trust you will not find presumptious.

I remain, Yours &c &c,
C. Pooter

Dear Mr Merton, April 21 '88

Allow me to express my thanks, and that of my wife, for obliging us with passes for the Tank Theatre, Islington, and we are looking forward very much to the performance of *Brown Bushes* and the accompanying farce.

Indebtedly, I remain, Yrs &c &c,
C. Pooter

28

The Tank Theatre, Islington

Dear Merton –   April 24 '88

With vivid impressions of our visit last night to the Tank Theatre embossed indelibly upon my mind, I take pen in hand to acknowledge my obligation to that one person who was the instrument in making our evening an experience never to be forgotten. Believe me when I say that *never* have we gone to a more *memorable* play than *Brown Bushes*. The passes you so *kindly* furnished us with having been issued by a previous management, we were *regrettably* unable to use them; nevertheless we were 'given' (or rather, were asked to *purchase*) an excellent box. Considering we had to *pay* for our seats, we did our *best* to apreciate [*sic*: the *Diary* notes with mortification that Pooter took Carrie's advice on the number of p's in appreciate] the performance.

Not wishing to presume upon your *long-established* connections as a man of business, the next time we have a mind to see the Play I shall not trouble you for an introduction but will deal with the ticket office directly.

Believe me, Yrs &c &c,
C. Pooter

The conclusion of his unsatisfactory negotiations with the Excelsior Assurance Office, and second thoughts concerning his regard for a paint manufactory, complete the first month's output of Charles Pooter's Ee-zee-kopi machine:

To SMALL CLAIMS D^{ept},

Excelsior Fire, Flood & Accident Assurance Co. Ltd
Dear Sirs,   April 25 '88

I acknowledge your postal order to the value of 7/8½d in 'full and final settlement' of my claim for damage to property whilst insured with your Company. Permit me to say that so paltry a sum might more appositely have been forwarded from the 'Small *Settlements*' Department than the 'Small *Claims*' ditto!

I notice, coincidentally, that in its advertisement on p. xxvi of the *Coal Exchange Register*, your Company makes much of its own '(no) small claim' of 'the promptitude and liberality with which the Excelsior Office meets its commitments.' I propose to invite the Proprietors of the *Register* to make it their business to inspect the testimonials on which this boast is doubtless founded.

I am, &c &c,

C. Pooter

[Pinned to this letter is an Ee-zee-kopi reproduction, liberally adorned with pen-and-ink exclamation marks, of the offending Excelsior advertisement – the earliest example of Pooter putting his machine to the same versatile use as the modern photo-copier (Ee-zee-kopi reproductions of items from the *Bicycle News* and other printed matter were found among his papers). The threatened letter to the *Coal Exchange Register*, if it were ever written, exists no longer.]

To Messrs PINKFORD,
Paint Mfrs & Artists' Sundrymen,
Blower's Yard, Molly Street, EC

Gentlemen –   April 26 '88

Recently, upon the recommendation of a friend, I purchased two tins of your new 'Empire' patent enamel paint (vermillion). I cannot praise this invaluable preparation too highly. Some flower pots which I painted have come up like new, as have the coal scuttle and the bindings of a set of Shakespeare, not to mention the servant's washstand, towel-horse, and chest of drawers. The paint certainly lives up to its claim to being 'quick-drying' and, having had bitter experience of inferior paints which promise the same but do no such thing, I shall in future use no other.

You may use this testimonial as you wish.

Yours &c &c,

C. Pooter

Gentlemen –   April 29 '88

I wish to withdraw, unequivocally, the testimonial for the new 'Empire' patent enamel paint which I sent to you, unsolicited, on the 26th inst. Whilst I will grant you that the instructions on the tin warn (in very small print, I might say) that the paint must be applied to a cold surface, and that it is not recommended for stoves or grates, no mention whatsover is made of baths. It should have been clearly stated that the paint dissolves in hot water.

Yours &c &c,

C. Pooter

MAY 1888

To:

The Lord Mayor of London – Lupin Pooter –
L. Cummings Esq. – Mr Rabinowicz, Tailor –
S. Sumpter Esq., of Peckham – Mr Farmerson, Ironmonger –
The Editor, Blackfriars Bi-weekly News *– Mr Biffen,*
Newsagent – Messrs Banff Bros, Riding Accoutrements.

Although, from what we know of him, neither more feckless nor reckless than the general run of young, suburban would-be mashers of the period, Lupin (Willie, as he was still known, at least to his family) Pooter must without doubt have been one of the prime causes of his father's loss of hair (See February 6 '89: To Kell Bros, Hair Growers).

Unusually, in his station in life, for a boy not yet twenty, Lupin at the time the Pooter Letters commence was living two hundred miles away in Oldham, Lancashire, having been transferred – perhaps 'banished' would be nearer the mark – to the main branch of Throstle & Epps' Linen Bank from their City establishment in Old Broad Street, which he had graced for a short period following a suspiciously brief spell in an insurance office.

Even before he unexpectedly turned up at 'The Laurels' for the August Bank Holiday – and, more significantly, failed to take his leave after the holiday was over (See August 6 '88: To the General Manager, Throstle & Epps' Bank) – Lupin's approach to his responsibilities cannot have seemed very satisfactory to the settled, industrious Pooter. The father's concern for his son is well chronicled in the *Diary* from August onwards. Long before then, however, Pooter was confiding his grave apprehensions to the gelatine bed of the Ee-zee-kopi machine.

Under the obvious influence of his 'Busy Man's Compact Library' edition of Chesterfield's *Letters* (it is among the books listed in the catalogue of household effects drawn up for the removal from Peckham), Pooter had embarked upon a somewhat self-conscious series of sermons intended to endow Lupin with the distillation of such lessons as he had himself learned from his experience of life. The first of these letters – the one believed to have been abstracted from its folder by Lupin because of its telltale reference to the theatrical magazine discovered under his mattress – was probably dated around the beginning of April, when the Pooters were just settling into their new home. There may have been a second one in mid-April – the 'Letters To My Son' seem to follow a fortnightly pattern – but if so, that too is missing. Thus, so far as this collection is concerned, the letter of May 1 must be regarded as commencing the series.

That, notwithstanding, was not the only correspondence of weight which Charles Pooter had to deal with that day:

To SIR J^{as} PEASE DAKIN, K^{nt,}
LORD MAYOR OF LONDON,
The Lord Mayor's Parlour, The Mansion House, City
For the att^n of the Secretary, Mr Eustace Gannon –
May 1 '88
Mr Charles Pooter is gratefully thankful to the R^t Honble The Lord Mayor for his most gracious invitation to a Ball at the Mansion House at 9 p.m. on the 7th inst, and on behalf of Mrs Pooter and himself has the honour to accept.
[The innumerable versions of this acceptance show minute variations such as a lower case definite article in the Lord Mayor's title, a comma between 'and' and 'on behalf of,' and every possible permutation on the abbreviation or part-abbreviation of 'Right Honourable.' It is impossible to say how many times Pooter re-worked his reply to the Lord Mayor's invitation, but at least twenty-nine drafts reached the Ee-zee-kopi stage, their preservation being thanks to Pooter's thrift in utilising their remaining space to copy short notes to tradesmen (see, e.g., May 5: To Mr Farmerson, Ironmonger) or brief acknowledgements of seed catalogues. The one here reproduced has none of this accompanying matter and so should be deemed the version received at the Mansion House.]

To W^m L[upin] POOTER Esq., c/o Mrs Postle,
3 Half Moon Street, Oldham, Lancs
My dear Boy,   May 1 '88
I take pen in hand to acquaint you with the proud tidings that your Ma and I have been honoured by an invitation from the Lord and Lady Mayoress to a Ball at

the Mansion House. It is, of course, a full evening-dress affair, and so your Ma asks your forgiveness if she does not manage to write you as usual this coming Sunday, as the Ball is to be on the Monday and there will be much to do. She promises a full account of the Occasion in her next.

I am sending you a fac-simile of the invitation, made on an Ee-zee-kopi apparatus – cannot show you the original, since your Ma begged leave to send it to your Grandma to look at. [Further proof that Pooter was keeping his Ee-zee-kopi extravagance from Carrie, otherwise he would surely never have allowed the invitation out of his sight (and quite rightly: the *Diary* reveals that it came back bearing a port-wine stain). Note, too, the indefinite article in the reference to the Ee-zee-kopi apparatus. Did Pooter not wish to admit ownership of the machine?] It is printed on very thick, cream-laden card in raised lettering, with a gilt edge – but, alas, these qualities do not show up on the fac-simile.

Now, Willie, it may cross your mind to wonder 'how on earth!' a comparative 'Nobody' such as your Pa comes to find himself among the luminaries of Trade and Commerce singled out for this great honour. Modesty forbids your Pa to speculate upon what supposed qualities – what presumed excellence of character, steadfastness of purpose, application, industry, reputation for honest dealing &c &c – may have recommended themselves to those who in turn recommend their candidates to His Worshipful the Lord Mayor of London. No such inhibitions restraining your Ma, she was good enough to say some words which I at once set down *verbatim*. They were these: 'However much you may be trampled upon at the Office by those who are not fit to clean your boots, this goes to show that your sterling worth does not go unnoticed.'

My boy, were we a family for samplers or pokerwork, I should have your Ma's testimonial emblazoned above our mantelpiece. There is something there for us both – for you and I, that is. Your Ma, shrewd judge of character that she is, recognises that howsoever her husband and son may 'hide their light under a bushel,' that diligence and

37

application which got them where they are in the world today, will ever drive them on to higher and higher things.

Now Oldham may not be the City, and its Town Hall may not be as grand as the Mansion House, nor may its Mayor and Corporation hope to match the Lord Mayor, Aldermen and Sheriffs of London for pomp and ceremony; yet I expect there are, from time to time, receptions, pie suppers and so on, where 'anybody who is anybody' in Oldham is presented to His Worship by way of recognition of what he is doing for the Town. Now you are as yet at the foothills of your profession, and still a very young man; but it would be a proud day for your Ma, Willie, should one of your weekly letters (which I am afraid to say have become 'weakly' letters – they are so slight and puny, and some weeks do not have the strength to arrive at all!) in due course be accompanied by a gilt-edged invitation card addressed to *her* offspring, for *her* to look at. Needless to say, it would be a red-letter day for your Pa also.

But my boy, such honours have to be earned – they cannot be plucked from trees like cherries. I have already listed [it is unclear whether Pooter here alludes to a previous letter or to earlier paragraphs of the present one] those virtues which, if they be lacking, make it ten times, nay, twenty times more difficult to make one's way in the world. Pray allow your Father to be so presumptuous as to offer some further advice for you to reflect upon – the gleanings, you may depend upon it, of much observation of, and cogitation upon, that vineyard in which we toil for our daily bread.

Your Ma, whom I have just consulted when she came into the room (and who sends her love, and you are always to wear a hat when out-of-doors in the chilly North), tells me that cherries grow not on trees but on bushes. But the principle remains the same. [This paragraph is crossed out. See below.]

Willie, as a future chief clerk, or, dare we hope, even assistant manager, of the Linen Bank, you cannot – should not – be unacquainted with the value of *stableness* in one's day-to-day affairs. I note from your last to your Ma (I still

38

await a reply to *my* last to *you*) that you have once again changed your lodgings. Mrs Postle's is your fifth address since taking up your position in Oldham. Whilst you may have the best of reasons for all this chopping and changing – this landlady proved a slattern, that one a 'nosey parker' (to use your expression), the place in Knacker Lane was not thought a good address by your friends, and so forth – be sure that this 'fly-by-night' attitude, as it might be thought, does not go unnoticed at the Bank, and will not commend itself to your superiors. I know you are punctilious about paying your rent (as about honouring all debts, however small – tho' I trust not ones of a personal nature: 'neither a lender nor a borrower be'), but to the 'outsider' it could be construed that you are in the habit of doing a 'moonlight flit.'

We will say no more about that: but there is another aspect of this frequent switching-about I should like to touch upon. Now your present lodgings, which I trust are clean and comfortable, are in Half Moon Street. Your previous addresses have been in Blue Anchor Street, Sun & Compasses Terrace, and Weavers' Arms Terrace, all of which seem to be named after public houses – doubtless the same hostelries which grace these particular thoroughfares. Knacker Lane is the exception, but there, as we know, you had rooms above the 'Three Horsehoes' Inn, and so it comes to the same thing.

My boy, you are in your twentieth year, and it would be unreasonable, not to say unworldly, to urge you not to take a drink. But I do urge you, for your own sake, to give public houses a wide berth. I do hope that your latest change of address does not find you spending your evenings in the private bar, much less the saloon bar – I will not insult you by even referring to the four-ale bar – of the 'Half Moon.' Public houses are low places, and not for respectable men of business, even when they are far from home, and even when their 'digs' are cold and cheerless (which it is to be sincerely hoped they are not).

Take a drink, yes – but drink *wisely*, in moderation, and in more salubrious surroundings than your 'Half Moons,' your 'Blue Anchors,' your 'Suns & Compasses' *et al.*

As to *quantity*, I would say the rule for a man of your age – I speak from experience, some of it bitter! – should be as follows. Spirits – that is, whiskey, brandy, gin or rum – to be taken never. Port or sherry – no more than the one measure, and that *only* on special occasions, such as Christmas last when I was more than pleased to assist you to a glass of my 'Manzanilla' (tho' less than pleased to discover, on Boxing Day, the bottle two-thirds empty. I have never mentioned this, preferring to believe Mrs Birrell the culprit). Beer or porter – half an imperial pint, of the bottled variety (you would not, I know, be seen carrying home a jug from the 'Half Moon'), with supper. Wines – half a bottle of claret between two, at dinner; or Graves or Sauternes (these are white wines) with the fish course – *but not both*. (That is to say, not both the claret and the Graves or Sauternes as the case may be – tho' positively *not* the Graves with the Sauternes, either, as your palate will know for itself as it becomes better educated!)

As to where these beverages ought – again I stress *in moderation* – to be consumed: let it be either in the privacy of your own rooms; or in the parlour of a friend; or in respectable supper rooms or chop-houses – but not in public houses, and most decidedly *never* in the music hall or gin palace. Music halls, as I was at pains to mention to you when you were persuaded by your acquaintances (I will not say friends) to pay that unfortunate visit to the 'Princess' at Highgate, attract, and are meant to attract, a certain class of person: and to that class, no son of mine does, or ever will, belong. (I am assured by my 'omnibus acquaintance' Mr Lawley, the traveller in Jopp's Gum-rot Paste – you have heard me speak of him – that the northern 'halls' are even more notorious, being spawning-grounds of shawl- and clog-dancers, rough 'comedians,' and men dressed up as washerwomen.)

Let me hasten to add, my dear Willie, that I exclude the Theatre proper from these strictures – indeed, your Ma and I, in the company of Mr & Mrs James, of Sutton, ventured to the Play not a few evenings ago, a business acquaintance having arranged for us to go. No: provided that the entertainment be wholesome and sensible – a tragedy, but not a melodrama; or a comedy, but not a farce – then there is much to be got out of an *occasional* (say, annual or bi-annual) visit to a theatre.

Yet whilst an interest in the Theatre is one thing, an unhealthy curiosity about all matters theatrical is quite another. I have already expressed my strong opinion of the periodical which I (mercifully not your Ma) found in your room when we were packing up to quit No. 17. Shanks Place. In the absence of any explanation from you – there may well have been, and even now still could be, a perfectly innocent one, if only you could trouble yourself to furnish it – as to why this publication should be found in the self-same spot where you used to conceal your 'penny dreadfuls,' I can only conclude that you were hiding it from parental eyes. Perhaps its presence under the mattress may be accounted for by your – mistaken, I do assure you [But see November 25 '88: To Burwin-Fosselton of the Holloway Comedians] – belief that I am generally antipathetic towards the Theatre. Should this be the case, then I am prepared to believe that you allowed that journal to come into your possession, and clandestinely into my house, out of that genuine, if frivolous, interest in 'plays and players' which you so often displayed when, in the immaturity of youth, you used to express a desire to go on the stage yourself – although against that, I would have thought that the journal's very title, *The Stagedoor Johnny*, might have given you some inkling of the nature of its contents. I will give my son the benefit of the doubt and say that as it did not, it is a testimonial to his inexperience of this world. And now I shall regard this unsavoury episode as closed, adding only that as you have a long way to go to your majority, I have a father's right to *command* you to heed the warnings I have given you.

Being uneasy in my mind, I have just this minute thought to consult the little 'Clarendon' *Gardening Manual* which I picked up off one of the Farringdon Road book-barrows the other dinner-hour. It turns out that cherries do after all grow on trees, as I made sure they did in the first place. This is very vexing, but I have not the time to copy out that page of this letter containing your Ma's well-meant horticultural 'correction,' and excise same.

Must close now to catch the post, hoping that you will take your Pa's words to heart, apart from the references to cherries. Will write again soon with more advice.

In haste to catch the post,

your affec^{t.} Pa

PS When I wrote that you must honour the smallest of debts tho' not of a personal nature &c &c, I meant to say that such debts should not be *incurred*, not that they need not be repaid – as certain of my colleagues, one of whom has owed me a florin and another sixpence for simply ages, seem to think!

Between this and his next letter to Lupin, the Lord Mayor's Ball was to dominate Pooter's correspondence:–

To L^{eo.} CUMMINGS Esq.,

'Longshanks,' Brickfield Terrace,

Holloway, N

May 2 '88

Just to give you word not to call next Monday, as we are invited to the Lord Mayor's Ball at the Mansion House. We shall be doing nothing on Tuesday.

C. Pooter

[There is no salutation. The legend 'Gripp's London Views' and a few minuscule words of printed text which show up on the Ee-zee-kopi facsimile, prove that this was written on the back of a picture postcard (an engraving – the photographic card was not yet common) of an ornamental drinking fountain in the middle of Peckham High Street. A note in exactly the same words went to Gowing on a view of the then new Peckham Eye Clinic. Evidently the economically-minded Pooter was still using up his old stock of Peckham views.]

To MR RABINOWICZ, Tailor,

47E Skellerman Bldgs, nr King's Cross

May 2 '88

Could you take out the creases in my dress-coat &

trousers, & repair the small tear in right sleeve, in plenty of time for the Lord Mayor's Ball on Monday.

C. Pooter

To Sebⁿ SUMPTER Esq.,
11 Mendola Terrace, Peckham, SE

Dear Sumpter,   May 2 '88

I owe you an apology. I made sure that I had *lent* you *Cassell's Book Of In-door Amusements*, and not *given* it you for the Tabernacle library as you – rightly, it would now appear – [There is no remaining record of this seemingly heated exchange] insist. My wife now belatedly recollects that in handing the volume over on the steps of the Tabernacle, I used the words, 'There is no need to return this. We have put childish things behind us, and I mean to spend these winter evenings learning Short-hand.' Therefore, I was wrong to ask for the return of the book, especially in so brusque a fashion, and I ask your pardon. Why not look us up, the next time you are visiting your cousins at Highbury Barn, and we will shake hands and drink a glass of port. Do not come on Monday as we are invited to the Lord Mayor's Ball at the Mansion House.

With renewed apologies, yrs most cordially,
C. Pooter

To Mr FARMERSON, Ironmonger &c,
18, 19, 20, Percy Row, Holloway, N

Mr Farmerson –   May 5 '88

I have it in mind to build a conservatory similar to the one next door, but larger. Can you give me a quotation? (Do not send round on Monday, as we are invited to the Lord Mayor's Ball at the Mansion House.)

– C. Pooter

[Nothing came of this plan – at any rate, there is no further reference to it – perhaps because of Pooter's subsequent chagrin to find that his ironmonger was a fellow-guest at the Mansion House.]

His ironmonger was a fellow-guest at the Mansion House

To THE EDITOR, *Blackfriars Bi-weekly News*,
The Steam Printing Press, Blakewell Street, EC

Sir –   May 9 '88

Your City Correspondent's otherwise excellent and comprehensive account of the Mansion House Ball, was marred by an unfortunate, although doubtless unintentional, oversight. In the list of guests, between the names of the Misses Pont, of Dulwich, and Dr A. Pope (representing the Cleanliness League), that of the undersigned and his wife should have appeared. The omission was all the more regrettable since the undersigned had ordered a dozen copies of your esteemed journal, to send to his friends. I trust that a correction may be made in your next number.

Yours &c &c,
C^{has} Pooter

A curiosity of the Pooter correspondence file is a sheaf of a dozen copies of the same letter, with the intended recipient's name yet to be inserted after the salutation 'Dear ——'. Like the numerous attempts at a reply to the Mansion House invitation, they owe their survival to Pooter's frugality in using the blank lower half for other short letters. Intended to accompany a copy of the *Blackfriars Bi-weekly News* (not merely a cutting of the Mansion House Ball report, which he could have adequately run off on the Ee-zee-kopi instead of going to the expense of a dozen copies), the letter reads simply: 'Just in case you did not see Wednesday's *Blackfriars Bi-weekly News*, the account of the Lord Mayor's Ball, which we had the honour to attend, is not without interest. Yrs.'

This is the only known example of Pooter using his Ee-zee-kopi machine to produce, in effect, a circular letter. As to why it was never sent out, we have to look to the remainder of his correspondence to do with the Ball:

To THE EDITOR, *Blackfriars Bi-weekly News*

Sir –   May 12 '88

I note from your edition of today's date, in the column

listing those personages who were guests at the Mansion House Ball, but whose names your City Correspondent unaccountably failed to take down, that a certain Mr and Mrs C. *Porter* were among those present. Perhaps your Printer was at the Ball, and had the pleasure of being introduced to this estimable couple. I can only say that my wife and I had the honour of being the Lord Mayor's guests, and did not come across the Porters all evening! I remain, Sir, in BLOCK CAPITALS –

Yours &c &c,
C^{has} POOTER

A further, agitated, letter to Lupin interrupts the Mansion House Ball sequence:

To W^m L[upin] POOTER Esq., c/o Mrs Westmacott,
11 Bird In Hand Terrace, Oldham, Lancs

My dear Boy,   May 15 '88

Your Ma has gone to stay with Mrs James, at Sutton, for a few days and so has been spared your latest letter – as I will dignify your half-sheet of scribble by calling it. I beg you to go back to Mrs Postle's at Half Moon Street and make it up with her, apologising for calling her an 'old trout' – that was unworthy of you.

Now mark! If you do not go back, and you have not left a week's rent in lieu of notice, then Mrs Postle may go to the Bank for satisfaction, and the fat will be in the fire. Your landlady had every right to complain – 'make a song-and-dance,' as you put it – at your getting in after midnight. Where had you been, by the bye? I believe I can guess – I expect *you* were the one executing the 'song-and-dance.' Please *read* my previous letter afresh – I did *not* recommend the northern music hall for a 'good night out,' but specifically and solemnly *dis*-recommended it – I know there is no such word but your Ma is not at hand to supply the right one.

I may as well tell you plainly, Willie, that she (your Ma) is getting herself into a state about your forever changing your lodgings – and that is *before* she hears today's news

46

of yet another 'flit.' In re-reading my letter of the 1st, pay particular attention to that portion dealing with this constant 'moving on,' and the dangers attendant upon a bank clerk living in the style of a gypsy. Be a man – return to Mrs Postle's and eat humble pie, or you may live to regret it.

In haste to catch the post,
your affec^t. Pa

To THE EDITOR, *Blackfriars Bi-weekly News*
Sir –   May 16 '88
May I respectfully draw the attention of that person responsible for the announcement, in today's issue, that Mr and Mrs Charles *Pewter* were at the Mansion House Ball, to the advertisement for Verity's Corrective Reading Spectacles in column five of the very next page. It is beyond my
[A second, equally incomplete draft of this manuscript letter, substituting the 'Enlarjo' Desk Magnifier for Verity's Spectacles, is also preserved, but there is no copy of a finished letter and so it must be presumed that it was never sent.]

To Mr BIFFEN, Newsagent & Tobacconist,
91 Proctor Street, N
May 19 '88
I *did* not order today's *Blackfriars Bi-weekly News*, and do not wish to take in this 'newspaper' again.
C. Pooter

From the *Diary* for May 22 we learn that having, during his Pinkford's enamel paint craze, incurred his friend Gowing's wrath by unsolicitedly painting a precious walking stick, Pooter purchased a new one and 'sent it round with a nice note.' If he made a copy of the note it no longer exists; nor does his reply, if any, to Gowing's thanks for so handsomely replacing 'only a shilling thing I bought at a tobacconist's.' On May 29, however, he wrote bitterly:

To Messrs BANFF B^{ros}, Riding Accoutrements &c,
2 Cramp Row, Oxford Street, Hyde Park, W

Sirs –   May 29 '88

Recently I purchased of your Establishment a silver-mounted stick costing 7/6d, as a present for a friend. I am now informed by that same friend that the identical article is to be had from the novelty arcades for 2s, and that I myself have been 'had.' Being, as a man of the world, familiar with the principle of *caveat emptor*, I do not seek redress. I merely say that should my wife take up riding on the Row, her habit &c &c will most decidedly not be supplied by yourselves, but we should favour with our patronage Messrs Cathbert's of Gt Portland St, who offer *value for money*.

Yrs &c &c,
C. Pooter

JUNE 1888

To:

Lupin Pooter – 'Housekeeper's Room,' Exchange & Mart –
S. Murchison Esq., of Crouch End – The Editor, Holloway
Journal *– L. Cummings Esq.*

An unsavoury address by the sound of it

JUNE 1888

The mid-summer found the Pooters settling nicely into their new home, but neglectful towards their writing bureaux. Both diaries for the period are skimpy, as is Pooter's correspondence. With many social obligations (Cummings and Gowing called 'every evening nearly' during the first week of June, there was a reciprocal visit to the Cummings' for supper and songs at the piano, and an evening when Pooter brought home his friend Mr Franching, a 'great swell' from Peckham, to take pot luck) and with the distraction of uncommonly warm weather (the Pooters and their friends twice 'sat out in the garden quite late') there was little time or inclination for letter-writing. Or so it must be assumed, the only other explanation for the sparsity of Ee-zee-kopi facsimiles for this period being that Mrs Birrell used them as firelighters during more inclement weather.

Lupin, as always, was the main target for Pooter's pen:

To W^m L[upin] POOTER Esq., c/o Miss Noyes,
Red Lion Yard, off Back Bethlehem Street,
Oldham, Lancs

My dear Boy,   June 2 '88
It was with mixed feelings that I received yours of yesterday's date. (This is the second of your letters to be postmarked from Preston, by the bye. Do you have friends there, and if so, why do we never hear about them?)

On the one hand, it is a relief to know that Mrs Postle does not have a claim against you for rent in lieu of notice, since you did not leave Half Moon Street of your own will. I am glad, also, to have your assurance that you did not use the expression 'old trout' to your former landlady's face, altho' I had sooner you had not used it at all. It is a most improper and insolent way to speak of a lady – *any* lady, be she never so lowly.

I advise against pressing Mrs Postle for a re-fundage of

two days' rent, or she may press *you* for the breakages. I counsel you strongly not to write to Mrs Postle in the terms you outline, or at all. Let it drop, boy.

On the other hand, I am dismayed to find you at yet another new address. You say that mine of the 15th was tardily forwarded from Bird In Hand Terrace, after 'propping up the mantelpiece clock' for a fortnight. Never mind that: the point is that if the letter had to be sent on, then you can have been in those lodgings for barely a week. That is a 'record' as the sporting pages would say, even for you. Your Ma does not even know that you have ever set foot in Bird In Hand Terrace, you were there so fleetingly – nor *must* she know. Any references to Mrs Westmacott and her shortcomings as 'Mine hostess' – I doubt not there will be some – must be for my eyes alone.

And so now you are ensconced in Red Lion Yard – an unsavoury address by the sound of it. If your Rake's Progress continues, soon you will have lived hard by every alehouse and tavern in Oldham. And, be it noted, with a *Miss* Noyes. I take it that Miss Noyes is, as we say, 'of a certain age' – that is, a respectable spinster? Understand, I throw no aspersions upon this lady's character – I am sure she is very charming and homely.

Mention of a lady's name – there is no other connexion! – prompts me to recall that I have been meaning for some time to offer you some advice on the fair sex and your dealings with 'our betters,' as they believe themselves to be! (Your Pa knows!!) I had meant to have a man-to-man talk with you on the topic, the night before you left for Oldham, but I had to lacquer my pipe-rack, and then your friends the 'Merrie Peckhamites' came in to say their farewells, and the evening was gone.

My boy, there would be little to be gained from instructing you in how you should conduct yourself with the ladies, were you never to make the acquaintance of any! As to how that is to be achieved, there is a 'right way' and a 'wrong way.'

You have never let us know whether you made use of Mr Sumpter's kind introduction to the Oldham Tabernacle in Tabernacle Street (one of the few thoroughfares in

Oldham in which my son has yet to take up residence! One wonders why!). It is to be hoped, in any case, that you regularly attend a place of worship – I am sure the Bank insist upon it.

Now I will not say that the primary purpose of Evening Service is to bring the two sexes together – it is very far from the case! – but I *will* say that the primary 'bringing-together' place for the two sexes is the Church, Tabernacle or Chapel. It was at a Harvest Festival Service that I met your dear Ma, as you have often heard her tell. We commenced our courtship soon after the Easter following, since when we have never looked back, nor regretted a day of it. Believe me, Willie, you could fare worse than to cast your eye about the neighbouring pews whilst at your devotions!

The sisters of friends, always provided that you choose your friends with care, often make suitable companions, as do cousins – but you have no cousins to speak of, certainly nowhere near Oldham. Properly-supervised societies devoted to some Christian or charitable cause – not amateur dramatic societies nor mixed bicycling clubs – may occasionally prove a 'happy hunting-ground.' Mr and Mrs Butter – you will remember the Butters of Crampton Street – met one another at the Peckham Rye Operatic Society. It is a pity you cannot sing.

I know of no other means of making the acquaintance of 'the ladies.' The park being positively ruled out, there is no remaining public place where a gentleman is likely to encounter a *respectable* member of the opposite sex.

As to how an acquaintanceship may be commenced, once you have decided to embark upon it, you will of course wait to be introduced by some *responsible* person known to both parties. Preparatory to such an introduction, the briefest of bows, *if reciprocated*, will signal your interest in one another. Should the lady *not* reciprocate, make no attempt to press your suit but cut your losses, and direct your attention elsewhere. Should the lady *over*-reciprocate, fluttering her eyelids and tittering, then the same rule applies.

As to how an acquaintanceship must be conducted, that

will be made plain enough by the lady's father or guardian. Except with his express permission, and then only if chaperoned, you will meet only under his roof and in his, or his nominee's, presence. You will not call upon the lady without leave. You will not smoke in her presence. You will rise whenever she enters or leaves the room. You will not bring her flowers or any other present except by permission of her father or guardian, and then only after a suitable time has elapsed. (It was a year before I gave your Ma so much as a bunch of daffodils, as she will tell you.) Encountering the lady in the street you will raise your hat and bow, refraining from detaining her in conversation.

As to those occasions when conversation *is* permissible, suitable subjects are: the weather, her parents' health, holidays, the doings of the Royal family, and general enquiries after friends. Unsuitable subjects are: politics, and the contents of the newspapers generally, the lady's *own* health in any interrogative manner (you may *inform* her that she looks well, but not *ask* her if she is well: ladies like to keep their illnesses to themselves), the theatre, and anything connected with business.

My boy, that is all I have to say about the fair sex for the present, and in any case it is getting late, and the last post 'waits for no man.' Do not fail to let me know what you find to do on those visits to Preston. I am very curious.

In haste to catch the post,
your affec^t. Pa

To THE EDITOR, *Exchange & Mart*,
170 Strand, WC
Att^n 'Housekeeper's Room' –   June 3 '88
What is the most efficacious way to remove blistered paint from furniture &c? A quick method would be preferable, as there is a good deal of it to be remedied.
C.P.
[Discounting the mis-spellings in the *Blackfriars Bi-weekly News*, this is the first and only known example of Pooter getting his name – or at any rate, his initials – in print outside the pages of the *Diary*. The issue of *Exchange &*

Mart for June 29 yielded the reply: 'We often receive this query, and have just as often answered it. There is a preparation, freely available, known as *Elbow Grease.*']

To S. MURCHISON Esq.,
'The Elms,' Elm Avenue,
Crouch End

My dear Murchison,   June 8 '88

It is a long time since we corresponded – you will see that we have moved since you last sent me your 'sale and wanted' list.

I thought you would be interested to know that I bumped into Franching last evening. I carried him home for supper and we had quite a chat about the old days. He remembered very well that you were wearing a pepper-and-salt tweed suit when I introduced you to one another outside the *Philatelic Times* offices in Booksellers Row. (Are you still a collector? I but intermittently.) He specially asked to be remembered to you should I write.

With every good wish, Yrs sincerely,
C. Pooter

[Telegram]

                                                June 9 '88

POOTER, LETTERS OF CREDIT DEPT, FIDELITY, OLDHAM. WHO MISS LIGHTFOOT, WHERE MEET? REPLY TONIGHT'S POST = PA

['Fidelity' was the telegraphic address of Throstle & Epps' Linen Bank. By having to include Lupin's department, for fear of the telegram falling into the wrong hands, Pooter exceeded the standard sixpenny rate for a dozen words, and would have had to pay eightpence.]

To W^m L[upin] POOTER Esq., c/o Miss Noyes,
Red Lion Yard, off Back Bethlehem Street,
Oldham, Lancs

My dear Boy,   June 11 '88

You exasperate me so much that were you here now, I

should shake you by the lapels. I ask you why you are forever taking the train to Preston and you say, 'To see Miss Lightfoot.' I ask you where you met this lady and you say, 'On the train to Preston.'

Will you be so kind as to elucidate *in extenso*, bearing in mind that letters, unlike the telegram I was forced to send you, are not charged for by the word? I am sorry if the telegram embarrassed you at your place of business, but with your propensity for shifting quarters, I could not be sure of reaching you at Back Bethlehem Street. At least I find you in the same place – that is something.

In haste to catch the post,
Yr affec^{t.} Pa

To THE EDITOR, The *Holloway Journal*,
Holloway Printeries, Printeries Corner,
Holloway Road, N

Sir –   June 12 '88
Is it not about time that the pile of gas-tar in Balby Street, which has been there since the road was dug up in early April, was removed? Walking to church on Sunday, I meditatively prodded at it with my umbrella. The gas-tar having melted in the hot weather, the umbrella sank in so deep that it had to be wrenched out. It is now covered in tar, as is the boot I had to press against the pile of gas-tar in order to get enough leverage on the umbrella.

Yours &c &c,
'VIGILANT'   (C. Pooter)

To W^m L[upin] POOTER Esq., c/o Miss Noyes,
Red Lion Yard, off Back Bethlehem Street,
Oldham, Lancs

My dear Boy,   June 15 '88
I refuse to believe what I read! Have you not ears to hear, eyes to see? Have you never taken in a single word that your Father has said or written to you, when he has tried to help you over Life's hurdles? Do I set down my

56

advice for the edification of your waste-paper basket? Did my letter of the 2nd, on your dealings with the opposite sex, go to line your hat with? Answer me, Sir! Do I talk to myself? I *demand* that you heed me!

Now. Let us calmly dissect the reply you have been good enough to write to mine of the 11th, and at gratifying length for once. At least you have been man enough to 'face the music,' and not to shirk my questions. On the other matter: it is not surprising that you find yourself 'a little short of the ready,' as you put it, in the middle of the month, when you are changing lodgings every week or so. Think of the expense – a cab, I'll warrant, every time you have to move your things. However, you are still at Red Lion Yard, and you appear to have taken my words on this subject to heart. I am enclosing a half-guinea postal order, which you had better spend wisely.

To the, if I may so, astonishing Miss Lightfoot. You say that you originally took a half-day excursion to Preston to see 'if it was less of a dump than Oldham.' Very well. My son is a much-travelled man, let us take the town of Oldham at his evaluation. There are no museums, no galleries, no parks, no concert halls, no monuments, no institutes for the advancement of learning, no shops, no emporia, no market hall, no tea- or cocoa-rooms, no places of amusement. It is 'a dump.' And so he goes to Preston.

In the railway carriage, you take out a cigar. No matter that your Father has advised you, that if you must smoke, to smoke a pipe – you take out a cigar. No matter, either, that there is a lady present in the carriage (its only other occupant) – you take out a cigar. Whereupon, your having no matches about you, she proffers a box of Vestas.

Am I going mad? Do I understand you aright? Am I to believe that Miss Lightfoot, unescorted, was travelling in a *smoking compartment*? (I had almost rather that you were smoking in the ladies' compartment!) That she carries matches about with her? In heaven's name, *why*? That she offers these matches to complete strangers? (There's our answer, I fancy!) And that you, a Pooter, accepted a light, from a lady, and struck up a conversation about – commenced to 'show off' about, more like – the stocks and

The astonishing Miss Lightfoot

shares market, of which you know nothing, and Miss Lightfoot must know less.

Your Ma has a severe head cold. If word of this business were to reach her, it would finish her off. *She must never be told*!

Willie, Willie, what were you about that day? Had *you* gone mad? Are you over-working at the Bank? A lady alone in a smoking carriage – and you take out a cigar! Where were your manners? Where were your morals? Why did you not call the guard?

You tell me that Miss Lightfoot is a nurse at the Preston Fever Hospital – a worthy calling – but that her people hail from Oldham. I wonder if they, or her Matron, have any idea how this 'ministering angel' disports herself in railway carriages (yes, I say *carriages* in the plural – you will not be so green as to imagine yourself the first young fool to be ensnared in this manner). A more censorious father than yours would write instantly to the Hospital Board of Governors. Being less than censorious – I mean less so than the hypothetical *more* censorious father I have just mentioned – I seek enlightenment, explanation, even exculpation.

Miss Lightfoot's home is in Oldham but she follows her vocation in Preston. I am to take it, I suppose, that there is no Fever Hospital in Oldham where she could have taken up her duties – that this is yet another of the amenities lacked by 'the dump' that is the town to which you owe your living? So be it. Miss Lightfoot, living much of the time away from her people, at an age when every young woman needs all the strength, security and discipline that *only* a steady home life can bestow upon her, every minute of the day, is as a waif caught in the storm. To whom, when out alone in the wide world between Oldham and Preston (or, on the return journey, between Preston and Oldham) is she to turn? The ticket collector? The railway porter? No wonder she is confused enough to sit in the wrong carriage – which I sincerely believe is how this pell-mell journey down the slippery slope began. She is carrying the matches by which she lights the ward candles. A young man steps into the carriage, produces a cigar, and she offers him the means of lighting it. It is what she would do, as a nurse. They are trained to help others. The young man is polite enough, and she is grateful for his company, and for the measure of security it affords her on her long journey. Who can blame her, when next travelling between Oldham and Preston, or Preston and Oldham, if she looks for a repetition of that comforting experience? It is like a drug.

My boy, I do not chastise Miss Lightfoot, I pity her. Yet I cannot say how mightily relieved I am to hear that your intercourse with her, since that fateful day, has been limited to sporadic, and for her part clandestine, conversations through the railings of the hospital grounds. We will say nothing of the money squandered on railway fares. Had this liaison gone further, the parting would have been all the more painful. For you must give her up, my boy. There is nothing there for you. Be a man – pay one more visit to Preston and tell her that it must be your last, for both your sakes, and then you shall have made a clean break. It is for the best.

Is the weather good in Oldham? It is so good here that at gone 9 o'c last evening, we were eating fruit in the garden!

In haste to catch the post,
Yr affec^{t.} Pa

To L^{eo.} CUMMINGS Esq.,
'Longshanks,' Brickfield Terrace,
Holloway, N

My dear Cummings,   June 15 '88

Could you spare an hour tomorrow evening – without Gowing, dear chap tho' he is, as it is about a serious matter? I have given some advice to my son, and I would greatly value *your* advice to me, should he decline to take it. It is a similar pickle to the one in which your nephew found himself in Birmingham. Believe me, you would oblige your old friend –

C. Pooter

To W^m L[upin] POOTER Esq., c/o Miss Noyes,
Red Lion Yard, off Back Bethlehem Street,
Oldham, Lancs

My dear Boy,   June 16 '88

Had you written *at once* to say that Miss Lightfoot had
'given you the jolly old chuck,' as you choose to put it, you
could have spared your Father much heart-searching; on
top of which, I should have saved myself an hour and a
half at my escritoire, and devoted the time more profitably
to stripping the paint off a chest of drawers. I am using a
preparation called, very cleverly, ' "R" Remover' (because
it makes *varnish vanish*). It is not the best paint and stain
remover on the market – that is 'Elbow Grease,' recommended by the *Exchange & Mart*, but nobody stocks it –
but it will serve. Tomorrow I shall start on the coal scuttle,
which is flaking badly.

My boy, I am relieved that this episode is over. You will
profit by it, believe me. I am glad, also, that you appear to
have thoroughly settled in at your present lodgings.

In haste to catch the post,
Yr affec^{t.} Pa

On that note, for the remainder of June, Pooter thankfully
relinquished his pen in favour of his paint stripper, all
unmindful of the time bomb that was ticking away in Red
Lion Yard, Oldham.

JULY 1888

To:

'The Curtilage,' Exchange & Mart – *Olympia Paint,*
Varnish & Stain Remover Co. – *M. Leach Esq.,*
'The Hollies' – *The Editor,* Holloway Journal –
Lupin Pooter – *'F. Pooter' Esq.* – *W.T. Tracey Esq.,*
of South Morecambe – *F. Porter Esq.* – *J. Nackles Esq.* –
L. Cummings Esq. – *R. Gowing Esq.* – *Miss Noyes,*
of Oldham – *Dr Hector M'Gallum, Freshfields Asylum*
for Idiots & Imbeciles – *Joshua Bagehot Esq., of Oldham.*

JULY 1888

The beginning of July found Charles Pooter without a care. After the anxieties of the previous month, which had kept the Ee-zee-kopi machine working overtime, he eschewed his usual fortnightly letter to Lupin – at least there is none any longer in existence – probably feeling that both son and father had had their fill of fatherly advice for the time being. Instead, he resumed his (on the whole) pleasant pursuit of those sundry minor interests which had perforce been neglected during the Lupin crisis:

To THE EDITOR, *Exchange & Mart*,
170 Strand, WC

Att*ⁿ* '*The Curtilage*' –   July 4 '88
How should I set about breeding Belgian Hare Rabbits in a small way?
C.P.

[The *Exchange & Mart* never replied to the enquiry – it may not have been received. Carrie (see her *Diary* for July 19 *et seq*.) objected violently to the Belgian hare rabbit proposal, hence if the postcard to 'The Curtilage' was given to her to post, she may have suppressed it.]

To The OLYMPIA PAINT,
VARNISH & STAIN REMOVER CO.,
Spratt's Wharf, Coffee Street, Borough, SE

Gentlemen –   July 5 '88
I have been employing your wittily-named ' "R" Remover' to strip the paint off several household articles. I am bound to say that the paint peels off easily, and I have no complaints on that score; however, once the surface has dried out after its final, liberal application of ' "R" Remover' to eradicate any remaining traces of paint that

may be ingrained in the wood, as recommended, I find that it is covered in unsightly, dark brown blotches, amounting to mottling. In other words, the stain remover itself leaves a stain. Should the preparation perhaps be diluted? It does not say on the bottle.

Yrs &c &c,

C. Pooter

To M. LEACH Esq.,
'The Hollies,' Brickfield Terrace, N

Dear Mr Leach,   July 5 '88

(If I may so address you, as neighbour to neighbour. We have not yet had the pleasure of shaking hands, but I looked up your name in *Staniforth's North London Directory*.)

Passing your pleasant, and very well-kept, front garden from time to time, I cannot help but notice the two fine laurel bushes which have pride of place in it, although your house is called 'The Hollies.'

As you may know, my house is called 'The Laurels,' but there are no laurel bushes. There are, however, two holly bushes.

Will you permit me to wonder whether, during the time the house was unoccupied before we took up residence, 'The Laurels' ' laurels, and 'The Hollies' ' hollies, in some way became transposed? It has been puzzling me since April. Pray forgive this intrusion.

Yours faithfully,

C. Pooter

To THE EDITOR, The *Holloway Journal*,
Holloway Printeries, Printeries Corner,
Holloway Road, N

Sir –   July 6 '88

May I, through the courtesy of your columns, enquire why the people of Holloway buy coals in summer? Twice this week, coal carts have come down my street, creating clouds of coal-dust which settles on my radishes &c. Yet nobody needs a fire in this blazing weather, and the coal to feed stoves and kitchen ranges should have been put by at the end of winter.

Can it be so that there are householders who allow their cellars to become so depleted that, without more coal, they could not cook? What if the coalman were on his holidays? They would be reduced to eating nothing but salads – which they would find covered in coal-dust! (from the coalman's previous visit, that is, before going on holiday).

Yours &c &c,
'VIGILANT'   (C. Pooter)

To M. LEACH Esq.,
'The Hollies,' Brickfield Terrace, N

Dear Mr Leach,   July 8 '88

I am pained that you should take up the attitude that you do. I did not, and would not, even think of suggesting that the hollies at 'The Laurels' and the laurels at 'The Hollies' were deliberately transposed. I say that if the deed were done at all, it was an act of inadvertence.

You inform me, and I am obliged for the intelligence, that in tracing a gas leak, workmen dug up the laurel bushes at 'The Laurels,' and threw them into the road, whence you lost sight of them. I would ask now, whether the search for the gas leak led also to 'The Hollies,' where the workmen might conceivably have dug up two holly bushes and likewise thrown *them* into the road. Later, ordered by their foreman to make good, but being ignoramuses in matters horticultural, they might have replanted the bushes, but in the wrong gardens – the hollies in 'The Laurels' and the laurels in 'The Hollies.' You, sir, perhaps employing a gardener, and being a busy man of affairs, may never have noticed whether the bushes in your front garden were hollies, laurels or red currants. That is all I suggest. I am sorry that you have taken offence, and as you evidently do not wish to pursue the matter, I am content to leave it there.

Yours faithfully,
C. Pooter

Such domestic preoccupations were interrupted by a seemingly innocuous postcard from Lupin; whereupon, feeling perhaps that he had been neglecting his paternal responsibilities, Pooter resumed the mantle of the Lord Chesterfield of Brickfield Terrace:

To W^m L[upin] POOTER Esq., c/o Miss Noyes,
Red Lion Yard, off Back Bethlehem Street,
Oldham, Lancs

My dear Boy,   July 9 '88

We were very glad to receive your welcome postcard with its fine steel engraving of Oldham Town Hall, which I confess I had never realised was a copy of Ceres' Temple in Athens. (I blush now to think that I once made a disparaging comparison between this noble pile and the Mansion House!) It is with satisfaction that I learn that you are still at 'good old' Red Lion Yard. Miss Noyes evidently does you very well.

Naturally, your Ma and I are disappointed that you won't be home for the August Bank Holiday, but as you say, it is a long way to come, and if your friend is pressing you to go to Morecambe Bay, then go you should, and enjoy yourself.

My boy, you have never taken a holiday out of the company of your parents, thus, although it is a long way off yet, you may wish for a few 'wrinkles' from a 'seasoned campaigner' who has arranged more holidays than he cares to remember. There, by the bye, is the first 'tip': a holiday has to be *arranged*, it does not simply happen.

As to apartments. These must be engaged well in advance, or you will find the best ones booked up. Not that you want the best ones, on your income. The nearer the sea, the costlier they be (I had not meant that to rhyme, but it serves to make it easier to remember). Nearer the station is best – cheaper, and within walking distance when you arrive with your luggage (otherwise it is tip – tip – tip, to porters and cabmen). But the best thing is to go by personal recommendation, or, as your Ma has just said over my shoulder (she may as well be writing this herself and be done with it!), you never know but that you are letting yourself in for damp beds. Your Ma reminds me that Mr Cummings has a friend who lives in Morecambe, a Mr Tracey, and so I will ask him (Mr Cummings) to write and see if there are any apartments he can recommend.

As to your landlady. Pray remember that you will be in her home, and so cultivate the manners of a guest, albeit a paying one. Talking of 'paying,' it will pay *you* to be civil – none of your 'putting on the Willie' – for you may wish those apartments again some other year, when she may be full; and that is when she will hold back a room or two for her favourites. Look at how long we have been staying with Mrs Beck at Broadstairs, who has never let us down yet – I put that down entirely to always removing my hat when crossing Mrs Beck's threshold.

As to meals. Take the full board – you may have to, if Mrs Beck's is any guide. Go half-board, and you are throwing shillings away in hotels and oyster bars. Take a bottle of wine in, and mark what you have drunk each day.

As to dress. This should be sober, but it need not be drab. The clothes you wear to business, but with a straw hat and a swagger cane, would do very well.

As to recreation. There is plenty to amuse you at the seaside – listening to the band, and so forth – without venturing into billiard saloons.

As to general deportment. You should behave in Morecambe as you do in Oldham. You were brought up a gentleman, and I need say no more on this subject, except – *no more Misses Lightfoot!!* (Needless to say, your Ma is no longer in the room.)

There is much else to be said on the subject of holidays, but the light is fading, and I should like to water the garden before retiring (no rain for 3½ wks – I hope you will fare as well at Morecambe Bay!). Will write again soon.

In haste to catch the post,

Yr affec^t. Pa

PS As to bathing. Your Ma has just put her head round the door to say that you are not to do any, as the sea may be treacherous up there. I am inclined to agree.

PPS Mr Cummings has just called – that puts paid to the watering-can – and he says he will be only too pleased to write Mr Tracey.

Blissfully unaware of what he had set in store for himself with that PPS, Pooter returned to his more humdrum correspondence:

To F. POOTER Esq.,
41 Cremorne Chambers, Embankment, W

Dear Mr Pooter,   July 10 '88

Seeing your interesting letter on the Channel Tunnel Question in the *Blackfriars Bi-weekly News* – a paper I do not take in, but I picked up a copy from the seat next to me on the Blue omnibus – I could not help but wonder if we are related. My father was Edwin Pooter, very well known in the City. His brother, Frederick Pooter (the same initial as yourself) went to Norwich, and they lost touch, tho' it is known that he married a Miss Hubbard. Perhaps we are cousins? Pooter is such an unusual name.

My own view on the Channel Tunnel, for what it is worth, is that we might just as well bring over the French Army on a fleet of steamers, and save ourselves the expense!

Yours faithfully,
C^{has} Pooter

To W.T. TRACEY Esq.,
137 Cadet Barracks Road,
South Morecambe, Lancs

Dear Mr Tracey,   July 12 '88

Our mutual friend Cummings has just come over with the splendid news that as you occasionally take in paying guests where personally recommended, while in no sense of the word running a boarding-house, you would be more than happy to offer accommodation to my son Willie and his friend, whose name I am afraid I forgot to ask.

70

Although responsible, and with a good head on his shoulders – he is with the Linen Bank at Oldham, who would not have taken him were he otherwise – he is not yet twenty, and it will be a relief to know that my friend's friend will be keeping a friendly eye on him. [Here Pooter encounters the same difficulty with the over-use of 'friend' as in his abandoned letter to Gowing on April 17, but it does not seem to have concerned him.]

The terms are so reasonable that I am quite sure that Willie will wish me to accept, with grateful thanks, on his behalf. Ordinarily I would not presume to speak for his friend, but since the rooms are already booked by the couple from Tadcaster you mention, to whom, in all fairness, you must give backword within the next 24 hours, if at all, I believe I may safely say that it is a case of 'where Willie goes, his friend is sure to follow.' I will make it abundantly clear that they must, as you say, 'take you as they find you,' and expect nothing 'fancy' – Willie, for his part, is used to good plain fare. I cannot see why being far from the omnibus route should deter them – they are young men, and what better way to work up an appetite than with a 40–50 minute walk to Morecambe Bay and back?

Believe me, my dear Mr Tracey, Yrs gratefully,
C. Pooter

[A scribbled – in contrast to Pooter's usual copperplate – holograph note on the facsimile reads 'News passed on to Willie last post,' indicating that Pooter was in too much of a hurry to run off a copy of his letter to Willie (it would have summarised the information contained here, though perhaps playing down the detail of the 40-50 minute walk to Morecambe Bay) and that for once he really was 'in haste to catch the post.']

To F. PORTER Esq.,
41 Cremorne Chambers, Embankment, W
Dear Mr Porter,   July 13 '88
I am obliged to you, and I am afraid I have been wasting

your time.

Strange to relate, the very same newspaper perpetrated the very same mis-print of my own name, in a list of guests omitted from a previous report of the Lord Mayor's Ball early in May, which Mrs Pooter and I had the honour to attend. When I say 'the very same,' I mean of course that my name was mis-printed as 'Porter,' where yours is mis-printed as 'Pooter.'

I am afraid you will get very little satisfaction from the Editor, who will probably refer to 'Mr Pewter' in his correction. I refuse to have his rag in the house any longer.

We must agree to differ on the Channel Tunnel, I am afraid. You say that the French are not our enemy – I say that they are, and I know them. A woman who used to make my wife's hats was French, as was her husband. They made off with the deposit on a country bonnet. A treacherous race, Sir.

> Yours faithfully,
> C^{has} Pooter

To W^m L[upin] POOTER Esq., c/o Miss Noyes,
Red Lion Yard, off Back Bethlehem Street,
Oldham, Lancs

My dear Boy,   July 14 '88

Your letter must have crossed mine. The 'A.1' Commercial Hotel sounds more reasonable than most of these sea-front establishments – perhaps *too* reasonable, they should be able to charge twice as much in that position, if all other things were equal. But in any case I have already got you and your friend fixed up with Mr Tracey. It is all in my letter. Besides, you know what your Ma thinks of hotels, with their billiard rooms and card rooms.

I am sure you will get on with Mr Tracey, who sounds quite an interesting fellow. He once bicycled to Land's End, Mr Cummings tells me, and never tires of recounting his adventures.

> In haste to catch the post,
> Yr affec^{t.} Pa

My dear Boy,   July 16 '88
    This is most vexatious. The arrangement with Mr
Tracey is made. He has had to turn away a couple from
Tadcaster in order to accommodate you and your friend,
and there can be no going back. You should never have
allowed your friend to book the 'A.1' Commercial Hotel
without consulting me first. You would put your Pa in an
impossible position, were you to let Mr Tracey down. He
is very thick with Mr Cummings – they have cycled
everywhere together – and would give him the whole
story. How could I face my old friend after that?
    You must write to the 'A.1' again and put them off.
Take care to give them a sound reason, as if they could not
let the rooms to someone else after you had cancelled
them, you would be liable – I believe it is under the
Innkeepers' Liability Act, or some such Act. You had
better tell them that you have scarlet fever. I know it is a
white lie, and I have brought you up not to lie – but it is
only a white lie, when you think what you might have
contracted on those visits to the Preston Fever Hospital.
That should satisfy them. And then let us hear no more of
hotels – Mr Tracey's it is, and tell your friend next time
kindly to obtain my permission before committing my son,
who is under age, to a contract he cannot honour. By the
bye, what is his name, as I promised to give it to Mr
Tracey?
                    In haste to catch the post,
                        Yr affec^t. Pa

After this slight rumble of thunder, the calm before the
storm:

                    To J^as NACKLES Esq.,
            [an office colleague who lived nearby]
        'Waverley,' Bamforth Street, Holloway, N
Dear Nackles,   July 17 '88
    Thanks awfully for sending round your 'spare' tomatoes,
and here, as promised, are a few radishes. I am afraid it is a
very poor offering compared with yours – when you said
at the Office you would send your boy round with a

Thanks awfully for sending round your 'spare' tomatoes

wheelbarrow, I thought it was one of your jokes! Has it
not been a grand year for fruit & veg?

Yrs,
C. Pooter

To L^{eo.} CUMMINGS Esq.,
'Longshanks,' Brickfield Terrace,
Holloway, N

My dear Cummings,   July 17 '88
   I am sending across a few tomatoes. Nackles, at the
Office, has a glut of them, and he has given me more than

we can eat. Rather than have Mrs P make them into chutney, I pass them on as a token of thanks for your kind intervention with Mr Tracey on my boy's behalf. Willie, too, is most grateful.

Believe me, my dear friend,
C. Pooter

To R^{chd} GOWING Esq., c/o Mr Mendelssohn,

19 Hospital Road, Holloway, N

My dear Gowing,   July 17 '88

It is ages since we saw you – I hope you are not still smarting over my remark about 'looking gift horses in the mouth' anent that wretched walking stick. Why not come over this evening and take pot luck? We are only having a bit of cold meat with some garden salad and a few tomatoes, but you will be most welcome. (Mrs P adds that there will be tomato soup, if anybody wants it.)

Believe me,
C. Pooter

[Telegrams]

July 18 '88

POOTER, BILLS OF EXCHANGE DEPT, FIDELITY, OLDHAM. QUIT RED LION YARD INSTANTLY STOP AWAIT LETTER = PA

July 18 '88

TRACEY, 137 CADET BARRACKS ROAD, S MORECAMBE, LANCS. REGRET MUST COUNTERMAND POOTERS ROOMS BANK HOLIDAY STOP LETTER FOLLOWS = POOTER

July 18 '88

POOTER, BILLS OF EXCHANGE DEPT, FIDELITY, OLDHAM. LETTER WILL BE SENT POST RESTANTE OLDHAM POST OFFICE = PA

July 18 '88
TRACEY, 137 CADET BARRACKS ROAD, S
MORECAMBE, LANCS. TELEGRAM RE POOTER
JUNIOR WAS FROM POOTER SENIOR = POOTER
[This confused rash of telegrams would have cost Pooter a
grand total of two shillings and tenpence halfpenny –
graphic testimony to the state he must have been in. Note
that Lupin's changes of address were not confined to his
lodgings. The move from Letters of Credit to Bills of
Exchange suggests that – not surprisingly, in view of
subsequent developments – he was being constantly
switched from department to department.]

To W^m L[upin] POOTER Esq.,
Poste Restante General Post Office, Oldham, Lancs
My dear Boy,   July 18 '88
   Now attend to me. 'For thine especial safety' (with your
interest in the stage – would now that I had allowed you to
go on it, instead of to Oldham! – you may recognise the
motto to be seen on the safety curtain) you *must* do as I
say.
   Willie – *flee!* If, despite my telegram, you have not
already done so, quit that place you are in instantly. Leave
your belongings (but make a careful inventory) – you can
send for them later. Go, boy, go! Go anywhere you choose,
I care not – Black Horse Street, White Swan Street, Green
Man Street, Fox & Hounds Street, Jug & Bottle Street, Gin
Alley if you will, but get out of that woman's clutches. Do
so now! I *order* you so to do! Not until you have shaken
the dust of Red Lion Yard off your heels should you
continue to peruse this letter. For my part (having
concealed it from your mother's gaze), I shall take a turn in
the garden to compose myself.
   I resume in the hope – the belief – that you have done as
I command. I take up my pen again more in sorrow than in
anger, William, to ask you but one question. Why? Why?
Why? Why? Why? Why?
   You believe yourself to be 'in love' with Miss – I cannot
bring myself to write her name. I tell you that you are not
in love. You are infatuated. She has led you on. Pah! The

76

'delicacies' you speak of – the black puddings, the mint balls and so on – were to one end and one end only – to ensnare you. Have you not heard the saying, 'The way to a man's heart is through his stomach'? Why else – ask yourself – should she trouble herself to bring pots of brawn to *your* room and not to the rooms of her other guests (if any – you never speak of any. Have you been living in that house alone with that woman? Answer me, sir! No – I take that back, my boy. I now remember you mentioning a Mr Bagehot or Bagshot. But why to your *room*? Is there no dining room, in which to consume brawn? It is a pretty peculiar establishment over which Miss Noyes presides, I must say).

Then you say she is 'a conversationalist *par excellence*' – that she is able to discourse on matters grave and gay, even on politics (she must know as much about that subject as that other lady knew about stocks and shares – nothing), that you 'talk for hours sometimes.' Silver-tongued siren! She descries a boy far from home, lonely, friendless – his business colleagues 'cads – none of them gentlemen' (your words) – and she leads him on with the voice of the Lorelei (the aforementioned siren).

As for that brazen scheme for spending the August Bank Holiday, I will say nothing, but that you have had a narrow escape. I will discuss it no further. I trust you are aware – you are nearly twenty – the nature of that which I will not discuss? I cannot discuss it. I wish now that we had discussed it when you were home – that I had left the lacquering of that pipe-rack for another time. The 'A.1' Commercial Hotel, indeed! It is a mercy, after all, that the pair of you did not take up those rooms at Mr Tracey's. I should have had to emigrate to Canada, like your poor Great-uncle Cecil.

My boy, when you yourself are older, you are bound to come across the expression, 'an older woman.' Always beware the older woman – she is desperate for a husband, will do anything – within reason – to 'bag' one. You say that Miss Noyes has 'a shock of red hair' – beware that too, it sounds to me as if it comes out of a bottle (the colour, that is) – 'which almost matches her red lips.'

77

Willie, Willie! No lady, if she *be* a lady, has red lips! Have you learned nothing?

My heart is too full to write more at present. Let me know at once that you are out of that house. I enclose sixpence in stamps for you to send a telegram (twelve words including our address – do not waste a word by including your signature) simply stating your new address. Wait! It would kill your Ma if she knew – if she even suspected – and from such an extravagance she would sense that something was wrong, and would try to get it out of me. No – you must send the telegram to me at the Office – the telegraphic address is Perkco. Just your address, mind – no mention of that lady's name, or of 'love' or any such nonsense. As to your destiny, and what the future holds in store should you continue along the path of folly, I shall write later.

In haste to catch the post,
Yr affec^{t.} & worried Pa

To Miss NOYES,
Red Lion Yard, off Back Bethlehem Street,
Oldham, Lancs

Madam,   July 18 '88

I write upon a delicate matter, as father and guardian of William Lupin Pooter, with whom you are acquainted.

Willie has confided in me his affection – I believe he means his gratitude, but he is but a boy who cannot yet distinguish one emotion from another – his affection, I say, for yourself. It is understandable – a boy far from his own hearth and home, with no friends near at hand, becomes (as young men ever will) infatuated with the first person to show him kindness and pity, as I know you have, and grateful am I for it. In his youth he misconstrues that kindness and pity, believing it to be something else. You and I see at once how ridiculous it is, when a stripling in the Spring of youth attaches himself to – pays unwelcome attention to – one who is in the Autumn of her years, and none the worse for that, I am sure. It is an old story.

As a woman of the world – by which I intend no

78

disrespect, meaning only that I believe I may address you as one mature person to another – I know that you will agree with me when I say, that it is better that he get over his infatuation alone (I am taking it that he is no longer under your roof). Willie has the absurd, romantic notion that he was to accompany you, over the Bank Holiday, to Morecambe Bay, where I imagine you must have relatives, on what I assume to be a half-day excursion. The 'A.1' Commercial Hotel, I believe, serves an excellent tea – but! I think not, Miss Noyes. It would only encourage the boy, as I fear your kind gifts of black pudding and brawn have done, to believe that you feel more for him than a motherly (if one may attribute such a sensation to a spinster lady) devotion. Besides, he is under age, and I must forbid it.

I beg you, Madam, as Willie's father – his mother would beg you as Willie's mother, did she know aught of this – to leave my boy be. Should he come round to Red Lion Yard to pester you with his attentions, I urge you to throw cold water upon his ardour. (That is meant literally – it has worked once before, when he fancied himself enamoured of an actress.)

Believe me, Madam, I am, your grateful servant,
C. Pooter

To W.T. TRACEY Esq.,
137 Cadet Barracks Road,
South Morecambe, Lancs

Dear Mr Tracey,   July 18 '88

I have the embarrassing task of asking you to take backword on the rooms arranged for my son and his friend, for the Bank Holiday. After all, he finds he cannot get a holiday from the Bank. As you have told me that you are in no sense running a boarding-house, but simply obliging friends, I will not insult you by the offer of compensation, but I hope it is not too late to offer the rooms back to the couple from Tadcaster, who originally had them.

With true regrets, I am, yours faithfully,
C. Pooter

To Dr Hector M'GALLUM,
Freshfields Asylum For Idiots & Imbeciles,
Salamandar Hill, via Reading

Dear Dr M'Gallum,   July 19 '88

As an Annual Half-guinea Subscriber, who had the pleasure of taking a turn with you around part of the Asylum grounds last Foundation Day, I am taking the great liberty of writing to you privately on behalf of a friend.

My friend has a son – a boy not yet twenty – who, being very highly strung, as well as depriving his brain of sulphur &c (he will not eat enough), is prone to irrational and impetuous behaviour. He has a strongly romantic nature – he does not take after either of his parents – which, in combination with the temperament I have just described, causes him to make unwise liaisons, from which he then has to be extricated by a long-suffering father.

My friend does *not* want his son committed. He is merely anxious to know whether there is any pill or medicine or other curative compound that may be obtained, which could be given to the boy (he could be told it was blood purifier or something of the sort) to quieten him down – put him on an even keel, so to speak, so that he is subject neither to undue elation nor undue depression (he is capable of lying in bed for days on end, staring moodily at the ceiling), but behaves normally, like everybody else. I would not trouble you, but the chemists do not seem to know of such a thing – all their preparations to do with the nerves seem intended to revitalise and inspirit the organs – the last thing my friend wishes to happen.

I should be ever grateful if you could advise my friend, as it is causing him a good deal of worry and sleepless nights. He wonders, indeed, if there is anything you would recommend for his own condition, which is one of permanent, nagging anxiety on account of his son.

I remain, dear Dr M'Gallum,
prospectively in your debt,
Yrs &c &c,
C. Pooter

To Joshua BAGEHOT Esq., c/o Miss Noyes,
Red Lion Yard, Back Bethlehem Street,
Oldham, Lancs

Dear Mr Bagehot,   July 20 '88

I am obliged to you for yours of the 19th, and for interceding on behalf of your Cousin, Miss Noyes, whilst she is indisposed, the quicker to make the true position clear, and to bring this unfortunate misunderstanding to a speedy conclusion. If I am the unwilling cause of her nervous condition, then I am deeply sorry, and wish Miss Noyes a speedy recovery with all my heart. I have a friend, a Doctor, who may be recommending to me some stuff that would calm her down. If so, I will pass it on.

I am afraid that all this has arisen because I have been incompletely, as well as inaccurately, informed – I should say *mis*informed – by my son. He gave me the distinct impression, reading between the lines, that Miss Noyes knew of his juvenile infatuation, and encouraged it.

It is the first I have heard that Miss Noyes is engaged to a Mr Gentleman, a pork butcher (the source, no doubt, of the succulent black puddings &c, with which she has so kindly regaled my son!). I did not know that Mr Gentleman, Miss Gentleman, yourself, your own fiancée Miss Tackling, your widowed sister Mrs Gordon, a Mr and Mrs Dickey, who are friends of Miss Noyes, and a Mr Stringfellow, a lonely old man who lives on his own, were to have made up – and indeed, minus Willie, it is to be hoped will yet make up – the expedition to Morecambe Bay. I was not aware that Willie was asked along as company for Miss Gentleman, who is but twelve years old; or that the 'A.1' Temperance Commercial Hotel, to give the establishment its full title, where the party intended – intend, again *sans* Willie – to stay, is owned by Mrs Dickey's brother, a Mr Jonadab Flick. I unhesitatingly accept that Mr Flick is a man of honour and a member of the Temperance Methodists.

I would instruct my son to take himself back to Red Lion Yard and apologise to Miss Noyes on bended knees, but in all the circumstances, I sense that she would prefer to let sleeping dogs lie; in which case, I offer Miss Noyes

81

If I am the unwilling cause of her nervous condition, then I am
deeply sorry

the profoundest apologies, for disturbing her equilibrium, of

Yours faithfully,

C. Pooter

PS I know of a good place in South Morecambe if ever you can't get into the 'A.1.'

To W^m L[upin] POOTER Esq., c/o Mr & Mrs Shabber,
216 Distillery Road, Oldham, Lancs

My dear Boy,   July 22 '88

Thank you for your telegram, and subsequent letter. 'What's got into you guvnor' was hardly the message I awaited – it was an utter waste of sixpence. However, it is all water under the bridge now. I have heard from Mr Bagehot at Red Lion Yard, and just as I thought, you have been making a fool of yourself. We will let it rest there. I trust your new lodgings with Mr and Mrs Shabber, who sound a nice couple, are comfortable. What do you now intend to do on the Bank Holiday? – your Ma would dearly love to see you.

In haste to catch the post,

Yr affec^{t.} Pa

Charles Pooter's diary reveals that on July 31, following a tiff with Carrie, he left her a present of a bangle 'with an affectionate note.' Either its facsimile has been lost or, perhaps feeling that some things are not for prying eyes, he did not make one. He did, however, record one letter for that day:

To Dr Hector M'GALLUM,

The Consulting Rooms,

Devonshire Chambers, Wimpole Street, W

My dear Dr M'Gallum,   31 July '88

I am very much obliged to you for your interest, but my friend does not feel that he wishes to have his son examined. Indeed, he is very much better. The son, that is – but my friend is, also.

With the grateful thanks of,

Yrs &c &c, C. Pooter

AUGUST 1888

To:

'Mr Zebedee' of Throstle & Epps' Bank –
L.D. Gomersall Esq., Throstle & Epps' –
Z. Ormonroyd Esq., Throstle & Epps' – Mr Spellman,
Fripps, James & Co. – Mrs Womming, of Broadstairs –
Mr Davidge &c, Perkupp & Co. – Mr Franching,
of Peckham – R. Gowing Esq. – J. Nackles Esq. –
Mr Lawley, Jopp's Gum-rot Paste – Sarah Pence –
Mr Birrell – Mr Sellers, of Islington.

Turned up unexpectedly to spend his Bank Holiday at
'The Laurels'

AUGUST 1888

On the first Sunday in August, the Pooters' wayward son, his Morecambe Bay arrangements well and truly quashed, turned up unexpectedly to spend his Bank Holiday at 'The Laurels' – with the announcement, incidentally, that he had 'cut' his given name of Willie and was to be known henceforth as Lupin.

What passed between him and his father, meeting face to face for the first time after the Nurse Lightfoot and Miss Noyes fiascos, is not on record: nothing of Lupin's amorous excesses was committed to the *Diary*, obviously out of fear that it might reach the eyes of Carrie. Probably little was said – the olive branch had already been extended in Pooter's letter of July 22, and it was very much in his nature to let bygones be bygones.

Which was as well: for an entirely new crop of potentially future bygones was already sprouting. Lupin had an even more momentous announcement than the one about his change of name up his sleeve. He reserved it for the late afternoon of Bank Holiday Monday, when Pooter warned him that he had better be thinking about catching his train back to Oldham. It was to the effect that there was little point in returning since he had, in fact, been dismissed from the Bank – that he had got 'the chuck.'

Pooter repaired to his writing desk at once:

To: —— ZEBEDEE Esq., General Manager,
Throstle & Epps' Linen Bank,
Corporation Street, Oldham, Lancs

My dear Sir,   August 6 1888
Pray pardon my ignorance as to your initials, but I have but one source of enlightenment, and he does not know I am writing to you.

Sir, my signature informs you of my business with you. I had made sure that Willie was doing well at the Bank, first being transferred to Head Office from Old Broad Street, and thereafter going from one department to another – steps up the ladder, as I thought them to be. It is a great shock to his Father.

I will not question your judgement in dismissing him from his post – I am confident that had you felt able to exercise clemency, you would have done so – but I wish you would set a father's heart at rest by telling me, in the utmost confidence, what act or dereliction on the part of my son, has led you to this grave decision.

Willie has not been himself lately – I believe, in retrospect, that he was too young to have been thrown out into the world as far as Oldham – and, being far from the sphere of parental supervision, has been subject to fits of strange behaviour. I am only too well aware of the usual reason for summary dismissals in the banking world – you will know as well as I do how the sub-manager of the A∗glo-R∗ss∗∗n Bank came to retire from 'ill-health' at the age of 45 – and my fears are that, in a moment of madness, Willie may, uncharacteristically, have succumbed to temptation. He has had some unusual expenses lately – tho' I do not say this in mitigation.

Sir, I should be ever grateful if you could see your way to allaying, if that be possible, a father's anxieties,

& oblige, Yrs &c &c,

C. Pooter

To L.D. GOMERSALL Esq., Under-manager,
        Throstle & Epps' Linen Bank
My dear Mr Gomersall,   August 11 '88
    I am very grateful to you for your letter of yesterday's date, and the information contained therein.
    I am more relieved than you know to learn that Willie was asked to resign simply because he took no interest in his work, always arrived an hour (sometimes two hours) late, smoked cigars in the Securities Safe, and had a reputation for lounging.

I believe that the experience will have proved a salutory one, and, Throstle & Epps' Linen Bank having 'licked him into shape,' that he will now settle down in some position in the City, where he will be a credit to his parents.

I am obliged also for the information about Mr Ormonroyd, and I shall write to him at once apologising for my gaffe.

Believe me, my dear Mr Gomersall, Yrs &c &c,
C. Pooter

To Z. ORMONROYD Esq., General Manager,
Throstle & Epps' Linen Bank

My dear Mr Ormonroyd,   August 11 '88

Pray excuse my unwitting impertinence in inadvertently addressing you by your Christian name in my communication of the 6th inst. Mr Gomersall has explained the position.

The unfortunate misunderstanding arose out of the fact that my son Willie, with that thoughtless irreverence of the young (he meant no harm), invariably referred to your good self as 'old Zebedee.' I ask your pardon,

& remain, my dear Mr Ormonroyd, Yrs &c &c,
C. Pooter

To —— SPELLMAN Esq.,
Messrs Fripps, James & Co., Stockbrokers,
Zinc Exchange Buildings, EC

My dear Mr Spellman,   August 11 '88

Forgive me if I have mis-*spelled* your name(!), and for being unfamiliar with your initial(s). You may recollect that we were introduced by our mutual friend Cummings at the Bicycles Exhibition in the Agricultural Hall two summers ago.

I am taking the liberty of writing to enquire, whether you could see your way to using your good offices to ascertain whether there may be a place for my son Lupin at Messrs Fripps, James & Co., in the capacity of clerk.

Educated at Peckham, where he sat all his matriculation

certificates, as well as only narrowly failing to win the Mrs Nellie Plack Memorial Book Prize for handwriting in his final year, Lupin first secured employment with the Mutual Life Insurance C^{oy} of New York, Cornhill, EC. Daunted in his ambition to be transferred to their Head Office in the States – he appears to have been misled as to his expectations – he resigned after some weeks to take up a career with Messrs Throstle & Epps' Linen Bank, Old Broad Street, in due course being sent to their Main Branch at Oldham, Lancs.

This was such a 'step up' for one of such tender years (he is still a year off his majority), that I fear, between you, me, and the gatepost, that advancement may have gone to a young man's head. Arising solely from his not unmistaken conviction that he could perform the tasks assigned to him in half the time allocated for their execution, he was, not to beat about the bush, dismissed for unpunctuality. However, all this is behind him now, he has turned over a new leaf, and I believe that the Under-manager of the Bank, Mr Gomersall, would be only too pleased to furnish qualified references, if required. If there is anything you may be able to do to give my son the fresh start he needs and deserves, you would earn the undying gratitude of –

Yrs faithfully, my dear Mr Spellman,

C. Pooter

[A holograph note at the foot of this letter reads: 'Sent same letter to Treskin, commencing "It is many moons now since I had the enjoyment of hearing you speak at the Peckham Mock Parliament." ' No address is given, but a G. Treskin was chief clerk at Hogburn & Partners, Milk Street, according to the Stock Exchange Yearbook for 1888.]

These weighty parental obligations discharged, Pooter turned, no doubt with considerable relief, to a more congenial correspondence. Despite his boast to Lupin (July 9) that 'Mrs Beck at Broadstairs . . . has never let us down yet,' their regular seaside landlady this year belatedly decided to let her whole house to one family, and the Pooters were obliged to take rooms with her neighbour, Mrs Womming. Correspondence confirming this arrangement no longer exists (perhaps Pooter left it to Carrie, who usually dealt with their holiday plans), but on August 11 Pooter wrote:

To Mrs WOMMING,
'The Cockpit,' Harbour View Terrace,
Broadstairs, Kent

Dear Madam,   ·   August 11 '88
   Just to let you know that we shall now be accompanied by my son, and so shall require an extra room. A back room would do, but will pay same rate for his board. We shall arrive on the train that gets in at 4.7 [on Monday, August 13] and so should appreciate meat tea as soon as we have got settled in.

Yrs sincerely,
C. Pooter

When the Pooter Letters were first examined, a mystery surrounding this holiday period was how they came to contain facsimiles of eight picture postcard messages, mainly of the 'wish you were here' variety, undated but manifestly covering the week at Mrs Womming's. Pooter could scarcely have conveyed the cumbersome Ee-zee-kopi apparatus to Broadstairs, even in the large assortment of trunks and portmanteaux which then accompanied most travellers on the briefest of stays – and most certainly not without it coming to the notice of Carrie, who would have supervised the packing. Had he had the Ee-zee-kopi crated up and sent down by goods train, there was no way of concealing his copying activities from his wife, with whom he would be sharing a room. He is unlikely to have put himself to the expense of renting a cellar or loft from Mrs Womming, who in any case, the Pooters not being among her 'regulars,' would probably have grown so alarmed at the presence of strange, clanking machinery and quantities of gelatine in her house – it was at a time when lodging houses seethed with anarchists – that she would probably have called the police.
   Neither, there being no jellygraph equivalent of the now ubiquitous photo-copying bureaux, could Pooter have had

facsimiles of his picture postcards run off at a halfpenny or so per copy. Writing the cards in Broadstairs, and then posting them upon his return to London after making copies, would have been out of the question – quite apart from the telltale postmark, it was quite unheard of in those days for mail to take more than a day to reach its destination: seaside postcards were expected to arrive mid-week, not the day after their sender's return.

There can be only one answer. The cards were purchased, written and copied *before* the Pooters left 'The Laurels' for their holiday. Did he, then, have a hoard of Broadstairs views, perhaps saved up from the year before? No – they were not Broadstairs views at all. The clue is in the ornate printed legend which the Ee-zee-kopi facsimile (all eight cards are frugally reproduced on a single sheet) clearly shows

The large assortment of trunks and portmanteaux which then
accompanied most travellers

emblazoned above each hand-written message – 'Gripp's
Comic Series.' This was a popular range of comic postcards
widely available at all resorts, as an alternative to local views
of horse-troughs and churches. London being then, as now,
itself a holiday resort, Pooter would have had no difficulty in
picking up all the cards he needed from any City kiosk. Given
Pooter's reputation for satire and making jokes, it would
never have crossed his friends' minds to wonder why he was
sending out comic cards instead of the usual tinted studies of
bathing huts or fisherfolk.

Since, unlike 'Gripp's London Views' (see May 2: postcards
to Cummings and Gowing), the captions to 'Gripp's Comic
Series' were on the comic picture itself and not on the side
reserved for correspondence, we know nothing of Pooter's
selection, except that it would have been in good taste. One

best-selling card of the day was a depiction of six seaside donkeys, with the legend, 'Now We Are Seven.' Pooter would probably have thought that disrespectful towards its recipient. More in his line is the policeman asking a check-suited masher to move away from the park bandstand: 'Sorry, sir, loud suits ain't *a-loud* [allowed] – they clashes with the music!'

Notwithstanding his 'white lie' advice to Lupin (July 16) Pooter was a stickler for the truth, and it is noticeable that nowhere in his pre-prepared postcards does he make any claim to be actually in Broadstairs at the time of writing, although he does not go out of his way to admit that he is not. Accepted picture postcard platitudes such as 'Having good time' are permissible, the more so since Pooter invariably did enjoy 'Good old Broadstairs' (*Diary*, July 31). The nearest he gets to deception is with 'Weather v. good,' but as it was an uncommonly hot summer, that too is perhaps allowable. As to why he wanted to go through the charade at all, the annual holiday was an important week in the Pooter calendar, and he would have wanted it put on record. Besides, the novelty of the Ee-zee-kopi machine had yet to wear off.

To Mr DAVIDGE [Chief Clerk] & All At Messrs
Perkupp & Co.,
Tinkers Rents, Cheapside, EC

Undated

Weather v. good. Broadstairs much the same as ever – would not stay elsewhere if you paid me! Nevertheless, shall envy Mr Spry setting off for Deal when we are just returning!!

– C. Pooter

To S. FRANCHING Esq.,
'Four Gables,' Stonequarry Terrace,
Peckham, SE

Undated

Spending a few days in Broadstairs *en famille*. Kind regards.

– C. Pooter

To R^{chd} GOWING Esq., c/o Mr Mendelssohn,
19 Hospital Road, Holloway, N

Undated

Good old Broadstairs again! This will not reach you until your return from Barmouth, but hope you enjoy(ed) your stay.

– C. Pooter

[Gowing was supposed to be going away with some Birmingham friends. In the event he unexpectedly turned up at nearby Margate, his arrangement having fallen through. There is no card for Cummings – he was at Margate already. (See *Diary*, August 15)]

To J. NACKLES Esq.,
'Waverley,' Bamforth Street, Holloway, N

Undated

Sent one card to the office but here is another one for good luck! Weather v. good – shall soon be getting as red as your tomatoes!

– C. Pooter

To Mr LAWLEY, c/o Jopp's Dental Cures C^{oy},
Upper Floor, Par Excellence Furniture Warehouse,
14–18 Albion Street, Elephant & Castle, SE

Undated

Blue sky of Broadstairs v. much preferable to the 'Blue' of smoky old London!!

– C. Pooter

[This is Pooter's 'omnibus acquaintance' referred to in a letter to Lupin (May 1). Blue was the colour of the bus on their particular route.]

To SARAH [the Pooters' maid] PENCE,
c/o Lizzie Pence [her sister],
15 Butchers Mews, Borough, SE

Undated

Having good time. Be sure to air beds.

– C. Pooter

To Mr BIRRELL,
11A Copenhagen Court, Female Penitentiary Road,
nr Holloway, N

Undated

Please to read this to your wife — having good time, and
she is to put down some 'Murderem' fumigating fluid for
the beetles first thing Monday. Sarah will let her in.

– C. Pooter

To Mr SELLERS,
11, 13 or 15, Yeoman Street, Islington, N

Undated

Can warmly recommend Broadstairs — would not go
anywhere else!

– C. Pooter

[It has proved impossible to establish who 'Mr Sellers'
was. There is no mention of him in either *Diary*. The lack
of an initial and the uncertainty about the address suggest
that Pooter did not know him very well, and was simply
using up his last postcard.]

Returning from holiday, Pooter was soon at his writing
bureau in more earnest vein. Learning from his friend at
Fripps, James & Co. that they could not find a place for
Lupin, he set about canvassing other stockbroking firms,
sending out an identical, slightly doctored version of his
previous letter (Lupin, instead of having been dismissed, had
now resigned because his mother worried about the effect on
his chest of the damp northern climate) to Poolers & Smith,
Pattles & Pattles, Merkins & Son, Freemantle, Seymour &
Freemantle, Renbrow & Nephews, Stenks & Marlowe,
Hopcraft & Peabody, and Septimus Bros. There were no
takers.

SEPT/NOVEMBER 1888

To:

R. Gowing Esq. – Silas Perkupp Esq. – Mr John Murray,
Publisher – The Editor, Jepson's Sunday Newspaper –
J. Whitaker & Sons, Publishers – Mr Franching,
of Peckham – The Misses Brackles' Agency –
T. Mutlar Esq., of Upper Holloway – The Editor,
Holloway Journal – Mr & Mrs Leslie Bird,
of Islington – R. Burwin-Fosselton Esq.,
of Highbury Fields – Rev. Selby Cole,
The Religious Tract Society.

Mrs Birrell, with maniacal zeal, was destroying all the paper she
could lay her hands on

'I should very much like to know who has wilfully torn the last five or six weeks out of my diary. It is perfectly monstrous!' Thus the Pooter *Diary* for October 30 – the first recorded entry since August 29. The culprit, it emerges from subsequent entries, was the incorrigible Mrs Birrell, who used the pages 'to wrap up some kitchen fat and leavings which she had taken out of the house.'

The Letters covering the same period almost certainly suffered a similar fate. It is inconceivable that Pooter would have neglected his expensive copying apparatus for two months at a stretch; that he was regularly at his writing bureau we know for a fact, for the *Diary* for October 31 reveals, on the subject of the missing pages, 'I am bound to confess the last few weeks would have been devoted to the record of disappointing answers received from people to whom I have applied for appointments for Lupin;' while annotations on the facsimile of his letter to the stockbroking firm of Septimus Bros on August 22, when he evidently resolved that it was a waste of his special copying paper to go on 'Ee-zee-kopying' identical letter after identical letter, show that between August 25 and October 27 he wrote to Sir Waldo Herring & Partners, Aringer & Christmas, Bagster & Bagster, Lubbock's, Hornibrook, Son & Almond, Merrick & Babcock, Foley & Puckle, and – a despairing deviation from the world of stocks and shares – the Employers' Liability Assurance Corporation.

That Mrs Birrell, with maniacal zeal, was destroying all the paper she could lay her hands on around this time is confirmed by Carrie Pooter in her own *Diary* for October 29: 'Upon going into the kitchen, found Mrs Birrell on the verge of ripping half the pages out of the latest weekly part of *Lady Cartmell's Vade Mecum For The Bijou Household*'; and again on November 11: '. . . the missing pages from his diary were torn out by Mrs Birrell, the charwoman, to whom newspapers, periodicals, *letters* [Editor's italics], bills, sheet music and even bound volumes are but so much butter paper.'

Although there are many palpable gaps in the Pooter correspondence, where the odd letter has been abstracted to mop up spilled gravy or ignite the kitchen range, the September-October interregnum is the only period where a whole batch of letters covering several weeks may be presumed to have disappeared. One letter only survives the Mrs Birrell holocaust. Curiously apposite, it owes it continuing existence both to chance and the fact that the charwoman could not read. Had it been acted upon by its recipient, this section of the Letters might have taken a different shape:

> To R^{chd} GOWING Esq., c/o Mr Mendelssohn,
> 19 Hospital Road, Holloway, N
>
> My dear Gowing,   October 9 '88
> You mentioned a lady in Mr Mendelssohn's second floor back, a former governess down on her luck, who you said was reduced to scrubbing and anything she could find.
> Do you think the poor wretch would consider it below her to do our rough work for 2d an hour? She could tell her friends she was the cook-general, if she liked. Mrs Birrell, who supposedly 'does' for us at present, is so stupid, clumsy and ignorant (as well as half-drunk half the time), that she *will* 'do' for us one of these days! (She nearly set the house on fire last week.)
> I have not yet mentioned this to Mrs P – she would say I was interfering – but she is as sick of the charwoman as I am, and, once I put it to her, will surely jump at the chance of having someone well-spoken and gentle to do the black-leading &c. Will you be a good chap and let me know?
> Yours sincerely as ever,
> C. Pooter

Besides this *cri de coeur*, there is only one other existing letter for the month of October, written *post* the Mrs Birrell onslaught. It reveals that Pooter's efforts on Lupin's behalf had at last borne fruit, though only by the intervention of his employer:

To Silas PERKUPP Esq., Messrs Perkupp & Co.,
Tinkers Rents, Cheapside, EC

My dear Mr Perkupp,   October 31 '88

I write with a full heart to say that I cannot tell you how thankful I am – how grateful I am – to hear from my good Master that he believes he may know of a place for our boy Lupin. That you have condescended to write to me, to this humble address, in your own handwriting, the quicker to allay a father's anxieties, is a kindness which I shall never forget, if I live to be 100.

I shall bring Lupin down to the Office at whatever hour of the day or night you may wish to speak to him. As you rightly say, Sir, with your customary sagacity, it must be impressed upon the boy that to be accepted into a Firm upon the recommendation of the House of Perkupp & Co., is to carry an awesome trust and responsibility. I will see to it that he does not let you down, Sir. Lupin is a good boy at heart, and I truly believe that he learned some valuable lessons in Life whilst at Oldham.

In deepest gratitude, I remain, beloved Master,
Your humble, faithful and devoted servant,
C. Pooter

The position which Silas Perkupp – rather surprisingly – secured for Lupin was with a flashy stock and share broker named Job Cleanands, later to abscond after the Parachikka Chlorates crash of February 1889. As for Perkupp himself, his continuing avuncular interest in Lupin was to have predictably unfortunate results, adding considerably to the volume of the Pooter correspondence (see May 14 '89, to Mr Crowbillon, *et seq.*). But that particular disaster was as yet a long way off. In the meantime, there was a diversity of other issues and interests to keep the Ee-zee-kopi machine busy, including Pooter's first small step towards immortality:

To Mr John MURRAY, Publisher,
Albemarle Street, W

Dear Mr Murray,   November 2 '88

As the review by 'Scrutator' in *Our Dogs* of General Sir Lance Paxendale's Memoirs, *Forty Years In The North-West Provinces*, may have escaped your notice, I am enclosing a jellygraph fac-simile of the same for your perusal. Not being a dog owner, I am not a regular reader of *Our Dogs*, but the periodical was put through the door by the paper boy in mistake for *Our Cats*, which my wife takes in. I would hazard a guess, however, that *Our Dogs* would not usually review a volume of this kind, its interest being in the fact that General Sir Lance, in his retirement, is President of the Chow-chow Society. That is why I thought this 'out-of-the-way' review might not have come to your attention.

Whilst not having looked at the General's Memoirs myself, I am bound to say, from the impression given by *Our Dogs*, that, with all respect, there seems to be little in them for the general reader not particularly interested either in Indian affairs or Chow dogs. But then what book of reminiscences *is* of interest now-a-days? More and more, they seem to be churned out by personages one has never heard of, simply to use up the jottings they have made in their diaries during the course of their distinguished careers (which I do not for a moment disparage).

Mr Murray, there are so many of these *ordinary* accounts of *extraordinary* lives on the shelves, that the thought – inspiration, if you will: it came to me whilst I was arranging my books upon removing house – occurred to me, how *extraordinary* it would be (or at any rate, unusual), to come across an account of an *ordinary* life, just for once!

Since April 4 last I have been writing up a regular diary of my doings, both as a householder at the above address, and as a senior clerk with a respected Firm of brokers in the City. Unfortunately, that portion of the diary for

102

September and October was destroyed by the charwoman, who did not know what it was, but much of the missing part could be written up again from memory.

I am sure that, once 'licked into shape' by one of your Editors, my diary would make an excellent book, of at least as much interest as the diary or reminiscences of any soldier or statesman, whose rarefied lives have little in common with that of the common run of reader. Indeed, it was with the object of publication that I started keeping it. There is not enough of it to make a book yet, being that it is for only eight months so far (six, not counting Sept. and Oct.), but at least you should be able to advise me whether it is worth carrying on. I have made up fac-simile copies of some typical pages, and these I enclose for your perusal. I particularly recommend the entry for May 7, which 'although I says it as shouldn't,' I think is an altogether first-rate account of the Lord Mayor's Ball, at which Mrs Pooter and I had the honour to be guests.

I have decided to call the volume, when finished, *The Diary Of A 'Nobody.'* I should be very interested to hear what you think of this title, and of my proposal in general.

Yrs &c &c,

C. Pooter

[Variations on this letter, usually commencing with some disparaging reference to the publisher's current list – the one to Cassell's, for instance, begins 'Congratulations upon having published not one single readable book this season' – were despatched during the next few weeks to Ward, Lock & Co., Smith, Elder & Co., J. Whitaker & Sons (see November 10), Chatto & Windus, Oxford University Press, Blackie & Son, Cassell & Co., the Religious Tract Society (see November 30) and the Homoeopathic Publishing Co. The book was ultimately published (1892) by Arrowsmith, Bristol, through the intervention of George Grossmith Jr, the comic actor, to whom Pooter sent the manuscript in a brown-paper parcel after being taken by Lupin to see him at a smoking concert. See 'How A Somebody Met A Nobody' in *Books & Book People*, March 1901.]

To THE EDITOR, *Jepson's Sunday Newspaper*,
Bodoni House, Bouverie Street, EC

Sir –   November 3 '88

For the favour of publication

As one who, in a year or two, will be celebrating his
silver wedding, I venture to put myself forward as qualified
to enter the correspondence following your article, 'Is
Marriage A Failure?' by 'Chanticleer.'

I believe your correspondent 'One Who Knows' came
closest to the heart of the matter when he said that, 'the
proof of the pudding was in the eating.' If the marriage
pudding be sour, or stale, or sad, or soggy – i.e., a failure –
then why are so many anxious to eat it?

'Once Stung,' by his remark that marriage is 'a bed of
nettles,' stands exposed as a cynic. Sir, marriage is a bed of
roses – *yet roses have thorns. There* are your 'nettles.' It
can never be 'roses, roses, all the way.' Who would want it
so?

With great respect to 'Juvenal,' 'Domesticus,' 'Kismet,'
'*Cave*,' and 'Simply A Ratepayer,' all, in their different
ways, appear to believe that it is possible to take out of a
marriage what has not been put into it – that the married
state should be a bottomless cornucopia. Sir, given that it
is not possible to pour a quart into a pint pot, how much
less possible it is to draw so much as a gill from a pint pot,
if that gill has not been poured in, in the first place!

'Pertinex' begs leave to ask, why, if the wedded state be
bliss ('like ignorance' – clever, but a mere play on words!),
no ladies have submitted testimonials to that effect, during
the debate. Ah, but they have! – if my own example is
anything to go by. Only last evening my wife and I talked
about this very subject [*Diary*, November 2], and we are
united – as in life we are united – in our conviction, and
avowal, that marriage has been no failure in our case. The
reverse: it has been an unqualified success. There is but one
testimonial: there must be thousands, nay, millions of
others – unspoken, yet there all the same.

That 'marriage is an institution, and those who enter
into it, should be in one,' is, I fear, an old chestnut; and

'Ethelred' does himself less than justice in disinterring it – for elsewhere in his letter, he is most perceptive and sensible in recognising that marriage is, after all, a partnership. To this, I would add: that 'give and take' is all, and that as regards the 'taking' part, the rough must be taken with the smooth; whilst as for 'giving,' I *give* you my word, Sir, that in the case of my own marriage, 'Mrs Vigilant' gives as good as she gets!

> Yours &c &c,
> 'VIGILANT'   (C. Pooter)

To Messrs J. WHITAKER & SONS,
12 Warwick Lane, Paternoster Row, EC

Gentlemen,   November 10 '88

I have to hand your letter of yesterday's date, returning my fac-simile specimen pages for the proposed *Diary Of A 'Nobody.'*

I accept with equanimity that you do not wish to publish the book – that is your privilege (and may yet be your loss!), but I do not follow the objection that you 'are mainly publishers of almanacks and the like.' If a diary is not 'the like,' then what is?

> Yours &c &c,
> C. Pooter

In mid-November the Pooters gave 'our first important party since we have been in this house' (*Diary*, November 15) to introduce to their friends a Miss Daisy Mutlar, to whom Lupin had (apparently unilaterally, so far as her own father was concerned) become engaged. Although it fell to Carrie to deal with most of the invitations, the event involved Pooter – and the Ee-zee-kopi apparatus – in a flurry of correspondence:

To S. FRANCHING Esq.,
'Four Gables,' Stonequarry Terrace,
Peckham, SE

Dear Mr Franching,   November 13 '88

We should be very pleased and honoured if you could

come to a party at 'The Laurels' on the 15th, at 9 p.m., to meet Miss Daisy Mutlar (Miss Mutlar's father is Mutlar, Williams & Watts). It is not too formal an affair – as before, you would take us as you found us – but my principal, Mr Perkupp of Perkupp & Co., may be among those present. The last time we spoke you said that you 'wouldn't mind meeting him one of these days.' Do come if possible.

Yours faithfully,
C. Pooter

To Silas PERKUPP Esq., Messrs Perkupp & Co.,
Tinkers Rents, Cheapside, EC

My dear Mr Perkupp,   November 13 '88
We should be most pleased and honoured if you would honour us by being our honoured guest at a party at 'The Laurels' on the 15th, at 9 p.m., to honour Miss Daisy Mutlar [Pooter does not seem to have noticed the surfeit of honours, though it is possible that he composed a revised version after this facsimile was taken]. Miss Mutlar's people, of course, are Mutlar, Williams & Watts. It is not too formal an affair – just a few friends with no grand people except your good self, should you feel able to come, and, we are hoping, Mr Franching, of Peckham, the business man, who has expressed a desire to make your acquaintance. We should count ourselves privileged should you be able to find time among your many social engagements to join us.

Believe me, my dear Master,
your faithful and obedient servant,
C. Pooter

To The Misses BRACKLES' Agency,
14 Knack Street, Leicester Square, W
November 13 '88
Please send us a waiter, properly dressed and sober, at 8.30 p.m. on the 15th, to serve at a party. Several

The other one

He must not be like the other one

important personages may be present, and so he must not
be like the other one.

C. Pooter

[This must refer to a previous function at Peckham. This
being the one oblique reference to it in all the Pooter
documents, it is to be assumed that it was never mentioned.]

To Silas PERKUPP Esq., Messrs Perkupp & Co.,
Tinkers Rents, Cheapside, EC

My dear Mr Perkupp,   November 14 '88
  I cannot say how delighted and honoured we are, that
you may come to our little party for an hour, should you

be able to get away from your dining engagement in Kensington in time. As always, dear Master, you are the personification of kindness towards

Your grateful, faithful and obedient servant,

C. Pooter

To T^{heo.} MUTLAR Esq.,

'Avoncrest,' 17 Atha Grove,

Upper Holloway, N

My dear Sir,   November 14 '88

Whilst your daughter tells us that you live quietly, and do not go out much in Society – you are a man after my own heart! – I hope I can persuade you, after all, to come to our little party tomorrow. I have just learned that my Principal, Mr Perkupp, of Perkupp & Co., will be coming, if he can get away from Kensington. Mr Franching, of Peckham, the business man, will also be attending. I think you would find it worthwhile.

Yours sincerely,

C. Pooter

To R^{chd} GOWING Esq., c/o Mr Mendelssohn,

19 Hospital Road, Holloway, N

My dear Gowing,   November 14 '88

If I have given the impression that our little party tomorrow will be an informal affair, perhaps I should mention that Mr Perkupp will probably be here, as will Franching, of Peckham – you have heard me speak of him. Therefore it would be as well if we did *not* play 'Touch nose, touch chin' &c – in case anyone thought of suggesting it.

Yrs sincerely,

C. Pooter

[There is no mention of this game in *Cassell's Book Of Indoor Amusements*. It was probably a piece of undignified nonsense invented by Gowing.]

To THE EDITOR, The *Holloway Journal*,
Holloway Printeries, Printeries Corner,
Holloway Road, N

Sir, November 16 '88

Many of your readers will have been following the debate on 'Is Marriage A Failure?' in one of your Sunday contemporaries. Nobody yet seems to have made the point, that in marriage, 'give and take' is all, and that as regards the 'taking' part, the rough must be taken with the smooth, whilst as for 'giving,' the partner on the distaff side generally *gives* as good as she gets!

Yours &c &c,
'VIGILANT' (C. Pooter)

PS I am enclosing a short report, for inclusion in your 'Residents' Doings In Holloway' columns, of a Reception held last evening at this address, which was attended by several notable personages.

[Pooter's only venture into journalism probably fell into the clutches of that most ruthless of all sub-editors, Mrs Birrell. No copy of the manuscript survives, and it was not published.]

To Mr and Mrs Leslie BIRD,
'North End,' Mercy Street,
Islington, N

November 19 '88

Mr and Mrs Charles Pooter heartily thank Mr and Mrs Leslie Bird for their kind invitation to the wedding of their daughter, Miss Elsie Edith Bird, to Mr Basil Rugge, at the Registry Office, Islington Green; and afterwards at the Believers In Joanna Southcott Hall, Newington Butts; and afterwards to a reception at Tuck's Vegetarian Chophouse, Theobalds Road; but regret that, owing to several previous engagements, they are unhappily unable to attend.

[Pooter had noted in the *Diary* (November 18): 'I am satisfied a life of going-out and Society is not a life for me; we therefore declined the invitation . . . We only met her twice at Mrs James's, and it means a present.']

The following letter to Rupert Burwin-Fosselton, a self-important member of an amateur dramatic society called the Holloway Comedians to which Lupin now belonged, who had inflicted imitations of Sir Henry Irving on Pooter and his friends, was provoked by 'a long letter from Mr Fosselton respecting last night's Irving discussion' (November 24) when Pooter had 'ventured to remark that after all [B–F's Irving] was but an imitation of an original.' Burwin-Fosselton's reply is recorded in full in the *Diary* for November 26. Although Pooter pronounces himself 'disgusted' by this response, there is no evidence of his continuing the correspondence. Burwin-Fosselton's letter concludes: 'Pray let this discussion cease with this letter. *Vale!*'

To Rupert BURWIN-FOSSELTON Esq.,
'The Bells,' Brace Hill Goat Farm,
Brace Hill (formerly Snatch Lane), Highbury Fields, N
Dear Mr Burwin-Fosselton,　　　　　November 25 '88
I have studied your lengthy letter to me, for which I am obliged, for some considerable time. As the pages are not numbered, and they may have been jumbled up, I have tried putting them in every possible combination – alas, in whatsoever order I peruse your observations on the stage and stage matters, I am afraid I can make no more head or tail of them than if they were in German.

I know not – I do not set myself up as a judge of good acting (although you are mistaken in your belief – your arrogant conviction, I would have said, did I not excuse your youth – that I 'know nothing' of the subject. We regularly go to the Play, and only recently enjoyed excellent performances by Mr Cecil Knell and others in *Brown Bushes* when it was at the Tank Theatre, Islington) – I know not, I say, how it is possible to argue – I take no sides – that an imitation of Mr Irving can be – *is* – '*better* than Mr Irving himself.' Surely, an imitation, to be successful, must be a *true* representation, 'warts and all,' as in a mirror. To exaggerate, or to build upon, or to improve upon, the characteristics of the original (thus, in your sense of the word, being 'better') must be to distort. And so I come back to my innocent remark, which seems to have

110

Whilst on August 5, I register my disapproval of my son wearing a
check suit on a Sunday

caused you so much offence, that after all your Irving impression was but an imitation of an original. Among amateurs, your skill as the Hunchback makes you non-pareil; but among professionals, I fear that you are a 'non-runner.'

Since you sign yourself just 'Burwin-Fosselton' – perhaps it is the fashion among stage folk and their followers – I shall follow suit and sign myself

Yours truly,
Pooter

To The Rev. Selby COLE,
The Religious Tract Society, 56 Paternoster Row, EC
My dear Sir,   November 30 '88

I am greatly obliged to you for your very encouraging letter in connexion with my proposed *Diary Of A 'Nobody.'*

I readily appreciate your fear that the fac-simile specimens submitted might appear 'too secular' for the reader at whom the Society's publications are directed. That is because, by a fluke, none of the examples sent for your approval happens to be for a Sunday. In fact, the entries for April 8 (the very first week), May 6 and August 26, particularly concern themselves with visits to Church, observations upon the sermon, &c, whilst on August 5, I register my disapproval of my son wearing a check suit on a Sunday. Other references on these lines, from memory, could certainly be worked in. Should you wish to commission the *Diary* for publication, I could undertake to extend these Sunday entries to occupy a much greater proportion of the material. I look forward to your further remarks.

I am, my dear Sir, yours very sincerely,
C. Pooter

DECEMBER 1888

To:

*The Directors, Great Northern Railway – P. Griffin Esq.,
'The Larches' – Dr Charles Kekswich, Chief Gas Examiner –
Mr Lawley, of Jopp's Gum-rot Paste – Mr & Mrs Birrell –
Mr Branch, Great Northern Railway –
Mr & Mrs Cummings – Mr Davidge &c, of Perkupp & Co. –
Mr Franching, of Peckham – Mr Farmerson, Ironmonger –
R. Gowing Esq. – Mr Gomersall, Throstle & Epps'
Linen Bank – Mr & Mrs James, of Sutton – Mrs Evangeline
Lupin – The Mutlar Family – Mr Otter, of the Luminous Fire
Extinguisher Co. – Lupin Pooter – S. Perkupp Esq. –
Sarah Pence – The Misses Tipper, of Peckham –
Mrs Womming, of Broadstairs – Mr Yeatman,
probably a bus conductor – T. Mutlar Esq.*

DECEMBER 1888

By December, the Arcadian euphoria of Brickfield Terrace had begun to wear off a little for the Pooters. The railway that ran past the bottom of the garden was becoming intolerable; the gas supply, as the nights drew in, was now perceived by Pooter to be less than satisfactory; and on top of this, new next-door neighbours – a large family called the Griffins – were proving tiresome. The festive month did not start well.

To THE DIRECTORS, The Great Northern Railway,
Rocket Chambers, Great Northern Hotel,
Kings Cross, N

Gentlemen –   December 1 '88

Before taking this house, you may be sure that I made a careful perusal of *Bradshaw*, in conjunction with a railway map, to see how often the trains go past. I satisfied myself that a frequency of eleven trains a day passing along the bottom of my garden, would be quite tolerable, and so it has proved. The night mail to Dundee sometimes wakens us, whilst during the hot spell in August, flying cinders from the 4.15 to York set fire to our grass, but otherwise we have had no complaints.

However, of late, an endless procession of goods, coal and cement trains has been going past at all hours – so many that my wife remarked to me that it was 'like living in the marshalling yards.' I have not been able to count up how many, being at business all day, but my wife thinks she counted twenty-three or twenty-four one day last week, not including the eleven passenger trains.

I am taking the liberty of writing to ask, why we have to put up with this nuisance – why can't the goods trains go by the same route that they used to take, by-passing our garden? – and whether it is to continue, because if it is, I shall most certainly pursue our landlord for a reduction in the rent.

I am, gentlemen, yours &c &c,
C. Pooter

To P. GRIFFIN Esq.,
'The Larches,' Brickfield Terrace,
Holloway, N

My dear Sir,   December 5 '88

I have yet to have the pleasure of your acquaintance, although I know that our wives have exchanged calls. May I welcome you and your family to Brickfield Terrace, and hope that you will find it as pleasant here as we do. The railway at the bottom of our gardens presents something of a nuisance just now, but that is only because they are diverting the coal and goods trains whilst replacing some of the track at the Scant Lane depot. They are working as fast as ever they can to complete this essential maintenance, and, contingent upon the weather, hope to be finished in late February, when the traffic should be reduced to the normal eleven passenger trains a day. I have this in writing from the Assistant Secretary to the Great Northern Railway, Mr Branch (I expect what we are experiencing is his 'Branch' line!).

To come to the point: a few days ago a Mr Elphinstone rang our bell, believing 'The Laurels' to be 'The Larches.' Ditto, a day or two later, when a Mrs Meld called. Ditto, two evenings ago – a gentleman whose name our maid did not catch, but who said 'he had come to settle up with Mr Griffin' [who was a fruit and vegetable wholesaler]. Ditto, yesterday afternoon – a Castle or Cassell family. Ditto, last evening, a Mr Steam, as I believe him to be called (perhaps, like Mr Branch, this gentleman is connected with the railway!).

Within the same period – as you will be only too well aware if you were at home during the relevant times – our new curate, the Rev. Simon Denny, called first at 'The Larches' mistaking it for 'The Laurels.' Ditto, a boy sent

116

round with a small parcel of earth from a friend, Mr Nackles (one of my plantpots had blown over, and he always gives me soil to grow things in, as his is richer in important chemicals). Ditto, the rag-and-bone man, whom I had stopped in the street and told off to come round for an old mattress.

I am sorry that you have had to put up with these intrusions, but you will agree that the nuisance has been less for you than for us, because we have been here longer and our friends know where to find us.

You have, it goes without saying, every right to call your house by so similar a name to 'The Laurels,' or any name you choose – even though there are no larches in your garden. Come to that, there are no laurels in mine (although there were, once upon a time). The garden of 'The Laurels' sports hollies, as you will have noticed, whilst the garden of 'The Hollies' along the street, boasts laurels. This already occasionally causes confusion among such visitors as go by the botanical evidence before their eyes, rather than the signs on our gateposts. A few months ago, indeed, a plumber we had sent for went to 'The Hollies' by mistake, where he had cut off their cold water and was dismantling the scullery taps before anyone realised that he had come to the wrong house. Think how much more confusing when, as well as 'The Hollies' being mistaken for 'The Laurels' and vice versa, 'The Laurels' is mistaken for 'The Larches' and vice versa.

I know that my wife has discussed this matter with Mrs Griffin, but I thought that as sensible men of affairs we could bring it to a mutually satisfactory conclusion. Please feel that 'The Laurels' is 'open house,' and call round for a glass of port whenever you are inclined, and then we shall discuss what is to be done.

Yours sincerely,
C. Pooter

[The battle between 'The Laurels' and 'The Larches' was never resolved – at least, not within the span covered by the Pooter papers – and relations with the Griffins steadily worsened. See December 7 and 19, and March 10 and April 14, 1889.]

To Dr Charles KEKSWICH, FRS, Chief Gas Examiner,
Pantry Yard, Whitehall, Westminster, W

Dear Sir,   December 6 '88

I have been advised by the counter clerk at the Imperial
Gas Company's offices, that you are the proper Authority,
under the provisions of the Metropolitan Gas Acts, to deal
with complaints appertaining to the quality of the gas
supply. Should I have been misinformed (the clerk was a
truculent and insolent fellow, who banged down the *Gas,
Coke & Light Year Book* with such a force that it blew a
cloud of dust in my face), I would beg you to accept my
sincere apologies and to have the goodness to re-direct this
supplication to the Gas Referees, who I understand to
oversee the gas companies under your supervision.

To address myself to the source of my dissatisfaction:
whilst a stalwart advocate of the superiority of the gas-
mantle over the oil-lamp, I have become aware, since
removing to the above address from Peckham, and thus
transferring my 'gas affections' willy-nilly from the South
Metropolitan Gas Co. to the Imperial Gas Co., of a
pronounced deterioration in the quality of the supply.

Whether this be due to a furring-up of the pipes, or that
the commodity in this particular district has farther to
travel from the gasometer, or that – as a colleague at the
Office avers [almost certainly 'that young monkey' Pitt, a
mischievous office boy] – the gas employed hereabouts has
to be diluted with an agent similar to paint thinners, as a
lot of it is sold to balloonists who find ordinary crude gas
too heavy for their purpose, I do not pretend to know.
What I am sure of, is that it is well-nigh impossible to
peruse the evening newspaper without the auxiliary aid of
a candle-lamp fetched down from my son's bedroom
(luckily, he is not a big reader these days).

In all fairness, it has to be said that my wife believes the
deficiency to be due either to the comparative darkness of
the house, or to failing eyesight on my part, or both. On
the first point, you will agree with me as a man of science,
the greater the darkness, the greater the power of any
incandescent device to illuminate it, and that once night
has fallen, it matters not whether the house faces north,

south, east or west. On the second, I have never had a moment's need of spectacles in my life. I would add, for your information, that the gas-mantles are *not* at fault, they having been thoroughly boiled in a vinegar preparation when we moved into this house.

I should be obliged if you would, on the one hand, instruct an Inspector to investigate the fault, or, if fault be there none, to be good enough to explain why gas of an inferior quality is charged for at, as nearly as makes no difference, the same rate as the superior brand obtainable elsewhere in the Metropolis.

I am, &c &c,
C. Pooter

The gas-mantles are not at fault, they having been thoroughly boiled in a vinegar preparation

It is grand to see your children playing on our party wall

To P. GRIFFIN Esq.,
'The Larches,' Brickfield Terrace,
Holloway, N

Dear Mr Griffin,   December 7 '88
I am obliged for your visiting card sent over with your maid, and the note on the back to the effect that as you have had a hundred of these printed, giving your address as 'The Larches,' there is nothing to be done. I would not, needless to say, ask you to put yourself to the expense of ordering new visiting cards; but perhaps we may review the question again when your present supply is running down.

I have also received your message about Mr Steam. I am sorry now that I made that joke, but I was not to know that he was in mourning for his sister.
                                    Yours sincerely,
                                    C. Pooter

Dear Mr Griffin,   December 19 '88
It is grand to see your children playing on our party wall – it makes one feel young again to watch them at their games. I say 'yours' – there are so many that some of them are probably friends or cousins?

I don't wish to appear curmudgeonly, but the pointing of that wall is very loose and dry. It would be terrible if any tiny tot were to be injured by collapsing brickwork – the more so since we are not insured against any person or persons falling off our side of the wall. Perhaps you are? I thought I had better mention this, as we have had some frosty days, and the top of the wall is very slippery.
                    With seasonal greetings, Yours sincerely,
                                    C. Pooter

But December is not all gloom and despondency in the archive of the Pooter Letters. His domestic responsibilities, though pressing, still left him time for amiable social intercourse – for instance, with his 'omnibus acquaintance.'

121

To Mr LAWLEY, c/o Jopp's Dental Cures C^{oy},
Upper Floor, 'Par Excellence' Furniture Warehouse,
14–18 Albion Street, Elephant & Castle, SE

Dear Mr Lawley,   December 20 '88

It is a while since I saw you on 'the old Blue' to Cannon Street. I expect you will be back in Fleetwood.

I thought I would drop you this line, to let you know about a most extraordinary coincidence to do with you. At Ribble's Dining Rooms yesterday I sat across from a representative of the Luminous Fire Extinguisher Co., who travels all over England for his Firm. We got chatting, and upon his mentioning Plymouth, I said that I knew someone who used frequently to go to Plymouth, travelling in Jopp's Gum-rot Paste – i.e., yourself, when you were their West of England representative. To my astonishment, this gentleman then said, 'Upon my soul – you don't mean Frank Lawley, do you?' Upon being told that 'yes, I *did* mean Mr Lawley,' he said, 'I have played many a game of dominoes with him. Please give him my regards when you see him.'

He has a beard the same as mine, almost, and is of the middle height. I expect you will know his name – I should have asked it, but I was so surprised that I spilled some custard sauce over my knee, and by the time I had finished dabbing it off he was gone.

With season's greetings, if we do not bump into one another before 'Xmas,

Yrs sincerely,
C. Pooter

A pleasant seasonal custom of Charles Pooter's was to scribble a few words on the Christmas cards he sent out, together with the recipient's name. This year he took the trouble to preserve Ee-zee-kopi facsimiles of these messages, carefully arranging their reproduction so that, as with his comic postcards from Broadstairs in August, he could squeeze in several to a page of his special copying paper. The fact that most of the names are ticked shows that the record had the secondary purpose of monitoring those who had reciprocated Pooter's Christmas cards.

The *Diary* (December 20) quotes Carrie as grumbling that 'the great disadvantage of going out in Society and increasing the number of our friends was that we should have to send out nearly two dozen cards this year.' In the event they sent out nineteen – all of them, even the one to Carrie's mother and to her closest friend Mrs James, of Sutton, being written by Pooter, but in some cases countersigned by Carrie. The four sheets of Ee-zee-kopi paper on which their felicitations are recorded in alphabetical order – Pooter having presumably been working his way through his address book – give us a charming insight into a Victorian Christmas. They were sent out on December 21 – 'to save the postman a miserable Christmas.'

To Mr & Mrs BIRRELL
[the charwoman and her husband]
Season's greetings from Mr & Mrs Pooter. Mr Birrell – please ask your wife to bring in a fumigating bomb for the back cellar tomorrow – Farmerson's will give her one if she makes her mark in the book.

To Mr BRANCH [of the Great Northern Railway]
Seasonal greetings from all at 'The Laurels,' Brickfield Terrace – which we hope will not remain a 'Branch line' much longer!! At least there is no snow yet to hold you up.
– The Pooters

To The CUMMINGSES
Our warmest good wishes for 'Xmas & the New Year. Good friends, good neighbours – it is grand not to have to slog over from Peckham any more to share the 'nuts and wine.'
– The Pooters

To Mr DAVIDGE & all at Messrs Perkupp & Co.
Taking *'stock'* of another 'Xmas, hope we will once
again have our *'share'* of good things!
– Pooter
[Perkupp's, of course, were stock and share brokers. It
seems unlikely that this was Pooter's first punning reference
to the fact.]

To Mr FRANCHING [of Peckham]
Warmest good wishes for 'Xmas & the New Year. I
dropped a line to Murchison at Crouch End ages ago, but
never heard back. Perhaps he has moved.
– C. Pooter

To Mr FARMERSON [the ironmonger]
Thank you for the colourful 'Blessing Bros Nails &
Screws' calendar, which now has pride of place in the
kitchen. A happy 'Xmas & a prosperous New Year.
– C. Pooter

To 'Dear Old GOWING'
So much hope you get 'fixed up' for 'Xmas Day – as
always, we are going to Mrs P's Mother, and the
Cummingses as usual will be in Bedford, otherwise a
convivial get-together would have been v. much on the
cards. Let us have it straight after 'Xmas & in the
meantime – all good wishes for the festive season from us
both.
C[arrie] Pooter   C[harles] Pooter

To Mr GOMERSALL
[of Throstle & Epps' Linen Bank, Oldham]
Season's greetings from all at 'The Laurels,' Holloway.
You will be pleased to hear that our dear boy Lupin
(Willie) has found a niche in the stockbroking world and
so is following in his father's footsteps!
C. Pooter

To 'Our Dear Friends The JAMESES' [of Sutton]
Wishing you all that you wish yourselves – health,
happiness, & prosperity in '89.
Caroline   C. Pooter

To Mr LAWLEY [of Jopp's Gum-rot Paste]
Just to wish you a v. happy Christmas. Saw the
Luminous Fire Extinguisher rep again in The Strand & he
is a Mr Otter. Said you *must* remember him & I was to
remind you about 'a certain evening at Mrs Banks'.' Said
you would know what he meant.
C. Pooter

To 'Dearest Mama'
[Carrie's mother, Mrs Evangeline LUPIN]
Will come down on the 10.20 on 'Xmas Day as usual –
do not get in any nuts as we have bought too many so will
bring some down. Season's greetings to all meanwhile.
Caroline   C. Pooter

To The MUTLARS
[the family into which Lupin hoped to marry]
May our two Houses – 'Avoncrest' and 'The Laurels' –
be united in happiness in 1889. Warmest 'Xmas greetings
from
The Pooters

To Mr OTTER [of the Luminous Fire Extinguisher Co.]
Sent your name & message to Lawley so do not be surprised to get a card from him – which you will have to reciprocate – more expense! Warmest greetings.
C. Pooter

To Lupin POOTER
A happy 'Xmas to our dear boy. Yrs in haste to catch the post –
Ma   Pa
(Now recall that as you are living here, do not need to catch the post!! Happy 'Xmas.)

To Mr PERKUPP
Respectfully wishing you & Mrs Perkupp a most jolly 'Xmas & prosperous New Year.
C. Pooter (Mrs)   C. Pooter

To Sarah PENCE [their maid]
Happy 'Xmas. Keep this card by your bedside to remind you to lock up *thoroughly* before going to your sister's on 'Xmas Day including coal flap (put iron bar across).
From all at 'The Laurels'

To The Misses TIPPER [Peckham friends of Carrie's]
Trust the seasonal weather is not too inclement for you, & that there is not too much frost & snow in '89. Warmest greetings –
The Pooters

To Mrs WOMMING [their new Broadstairs landlady]
'Seasonal' ('Xmas) greetings & good wishes for an excellent 'season' (summer) when hope to see you again. Expect good old Broadstairs looks v. different in winter.
Mr & Mrs C. Pooter

To Mr YEATMAN [?]

Here's hoping you enjoy your 'Xmas 'fare'!

[Like the Broadstairs postcard to a Mr Sellers, this card remains a mystery. From the quotation marks and exclamation mark, 'fare' is evidently a pun, suggesting that Mr Yeatman might have been Pooter's regular bus conductor.]

After all these pleasantries it was a pity that the first year of the Pooter Letters had to end on a sour note. Pursuing his stormy courtship of Daisy Mutlar – very much an on-off affair – Lupin Pooter (*Diary*, December 30) had felt 'obliged to take her old fool of a father down a peg.' On New Year's Eve, Charles Pooter received a letter from Mr Mutlar forbidding Lupin the house. Highly satirical in tone, it might have been written by Pooter himself; but while thoroughly appreciative of his own flair for sustained irony, he often failed to recognise the quality in others. With heavy heart he sat down to pen his last letter for 1888:

To T^{heo.} MUTLAR Esq.,
'Avoncrest,' 17 Atha Grove,
Upper Holloway, N

My dear Sir,   December 31 '88

I am very sad that you have felt obliged to forbid my son to enter your house ever again – the more so because you are big enough to say that it deprives you of the society of 'one of the most modest, unassuming and gentlemanly persons you have ever had the honour of being acquainted with.' So handsome a testimonial makes a father feel proud, and it is a shame that your dilemma, which I quite understand, as to 'who is to be the Master in your own house – yourself or Lupin?', could only be resolved in this way. Lupin is a boy wishing to be a man – I believe that there are among us, men wishing to be boys – that is, who are envious of, and therefore impatient with, the impetuousness and effervescence of youth. It is not surprising that you are critical of him – I am myself, sometimes – but, as you yourself so generously admit, he has qualities which many of his elders could profitably emulate. I hope you will re-consider your decision and that this rift will not last. Meanwhile, almost upon the stroke of midnight, I wish you and Mrs Mutlar a happy and tranquil New Year.

Yours sincerely,

C. Pooter

JANUARY 1889

To:

Lupin Pooter – L.D. Gomersall Esq., Throstle & Epps'
Linen Bank – Mr Lawley, of Jopp's Gum-rot Paste –
Silas Perkupp Esq. – Jerome K. Jerome Esq. –
The Ee-zee-kopi Co. – R. Gowing Esq.

JANUARY 1889

With the return of Lupin to the bosom of his family at the beginning of August, it might be assumed that there would be no more 'Letters To My Son' in the Pooter file. Nor are there – until New Year's Day. This solitary (until July 10, by which time Lupin had left home again) example kindles the suspicion that there may have been others – that Pooter, when exasperated beyond endurance by Lupin's erratic behaviour, was apt to transcribe a piece of his mind into copperplate and leave it propped up against his wayward son's breakfast egg (Lupin was notoriously a late riser). If so, we have either Mrs Birrell or Lupin himself to thank for the absence of any continuing flow of advice and injunction from the parental pen.

But that is speculation. The one thing we do know for certain is that on the first day of 1889, Lupin having neglected to make any New Year Resolutions for himself, Charles Pooter sat down at his writing bureau and made them for him:

To Lupin POOTER Esq.,
'The Laurels,' Brickfield Terrace,
Holloway, N

My dear Boy,   January 1 '89
    The New Year is upon us – a fresh page in the Journal of our lives, and a time for reflection.

Inside the New Year card your Ma sent to Mr and Mrs Treane [After his exertions over the Christmas cards, Pooter appears to have delegated to Carrie the chore of sending out New Year cards to such obscure acquaintances as they had dropped from their list, but who had embarrassingly neglected to drop the Pooters from theirs], I came across a sentiment so striking and apposite, that I copied it out. Here it is:

Time is our Teacher in the School of Life –
And each Glad New Year, a Term's beginning

Lupin – Willie, as we shall ever think of you – you are all but grown to man's estate – yet you are but in the kindergarten of the School of Life, with many a lesson yet to be learned. At the 'Term's beginning,' may a fond father – for all that he is not *quite* of an age with Old Father Time! – set your 'curriculum' of good Resolutions? They are:

1. That, *should* you elect to stay out until the household has gone to bed (and I wish you would not *always* do so), you will not re-light the gas in the parlour. It is bad for the mantle – heating it up again when it has not gone cold can crack the glass, that is a scientific fact – and wasteful of gas, the more so when you omit to turn it off again. If you wish to read, there is a perfectly good candle-lamp in your room. (If it is not in your room, you will find it on my desk.)

2. That you will not sing about the house – particularly during the hour just mentioned, and *most* particularly not the ditty you came home with two nights ago – you know very well which I mean, the one that ends each verse with, 'And after that he never was the same again.'

3. That you will not smoke in your room, or, if you must smoke in your room, that you will not smoke in bed, particularly upon getting home at all hours.

4. That you will rise promptly, and not have to go to business on cold coffee, stale toast and a congealed egg – as will certainly from now on be the case, Sarah having been instructed that *her* New Year Resolution is not to wait hand and foot on 'the young Master' when it pleases him to come down, but to serve his breakfast at the appointed hour, and no later.

5. That you will defer to your elders (I will not say betters: we lay no claim to be that) in all things, and will *not* be familiar. There is a saying, that 'familiarity breeds contempt.' Yes, sir! – contempt *of* him who is over-familiar, *by* him that is the object of that over-familiarity. (I have had a letter from Mr Mutlar, which I shall wish to speak to you about presently. I had thought him to be singing your praises, in part, but upon re-reading it again this morning, I find that he is being sarcastic.)

6. That you will remind yourself of what I wrote you, when you were at Oldham, upon the topic of Drink. Should you have mislàid my letter, I can furnish you with a copy, which I earnestly advise you to read. [This may have alerted Lupin to the existence of the Ee-zee-kopi record of the Oldham correspondence which he subsequently tracked down and 'edited.'] You are swilling down whiskey, these days, as if it were shandy-gaff.

7. That, whilst you are under my roof, you will shoulder your portion of household tasks normally undertaken by the man, or men, of the house – e.g., untangling the Venetian blinds &c. Your Ma nearly tripped on a loose stair-rod yesterday – I have had it down on my list of things to mend, but you must have noticed the stair-rod clip working loose, and there is no reason why *you* should not have attended to it. (I will introduce you to a tool-box of my acquaintance!)

I had meant to make this a set of ten Resolutions – it would have been neater – but a glance at the clock tells me that I must close now to catch the post, and so I shall leave you, my boy, to reflect upon 'the art of self-improvement' and compose the other three yourself.

Wishing you the happiest of New Years,

As ever, Yr affec^{t.} Pa

PS When I say I have to catch the post, naturally I don't mean with this letter – that would be a waste of a stamp – but another which I have to write.

To L.D. GOMERSALL Esq., Under-manager,
Throstle & Epps' Linen Bank,
Corporation Street, Oldham, Lancs

Dear Mr Gomersall,   January 1 '89

My wife has only just informed me that she has sent you a New Year card, in the mistaken belief that we did not send you a Christmas card. As you will know, such is not the case. I thought I should mention this, in case you felt any obligation to reciprocate our New Year card. There is no need for that – your 'Xmas card of Bog Moor in the snow will do very nicely. (But if you have already sent a

133

New Year card, it would be most welcome.)
Yours in haste to catch the post,
C. Pooter

To Mr LAWLEY, c/o Jopp's Dental Cures C^{oy},
Upper Floor, 'Par Excellence' Furniture Warehouse,
14–18 Albion Street, Elephant & Castle, SE

Dear Mr Lawley,   January 2 '89

When I passed on Mr Otter's message that you must remember 'a certain evening at Mrs Banks',' I did not anticipate a description of it from you, however veiled. I most earnestly caution you against writing that kind of thing on the Firm's letter-heading. I decidedly would *not* wish to meet the lady, should I ever get down to Weston-super-Mare; nor do I suppose that you and I shall be meeting again on the Blue 'bus, as I shall in future take the Green.

Yours sincerely,
C. Pooter

To Silas PERKUPP Esq., Messrs Perkupp & Co.,
Tinkers Rents, Cheapside, EC

My dear Mr Perkupp,   January 5 '89

When you did me the honour of telling me that I was to be made a senior clerk, and what my new salary – undeserved – was to be, I was so overwhelmed that words failed me. Never, in all my 21 years of devoted service to my beloved Master, have I been so near to breaking down. I express now that humble, heartfelt gratitude which, in my wretched, stumbling way, I fear I failed to convey to your good self in person. That I shall ever strive to be worthy of the confidence and trust you have placed in me need not be said – that I can never be worthy of the *value* you have placed upon my services, *must* be said. A half – a quarter – of the most generous increase any man has ever been given, would have been ample and more.

I have the honour to be, my good Master,
Your humble, faithful, grateful and devoted
servant, now and forever,
C. Pooter

Pooter's unprecedented raise of £100 a year, at a time when good champagne could be had for forty shillings a dozen (Jackson Frères, which Pooter took to drinking regularly after his windfall, would have been considerably cheaper), may have gone to his head a little – or perhaps the Jackson Frères did. At any rate, the die-stamped stationery of 'The Laurels' for once sought more exalted company than usual:

To Jerome K. JEROME Esq.,
c/o Messrs J.W. Arrowsmith, Publishers,
Quay Street, Bristol

Dear Mr Jerome K. Jerome,   January 6 '89
   As one who is very familiar with your works – my son forever has his nose in your 'stage' books – I venture to take the liberty of writing to you re the announcement, by 'Bookworm' in *Jepson's Sunday Newspaper*, that you contemplate publishing an account of a boating holiday.
   To quote Mr Punch's 'Advice to persons about to marry' – 'Don't!' Although not yet a published author myself, I do have in mind a book of my own – nothing in your line – and so I know whereof I speak. The boating craze will soon be over, and in any case is certainly not worth a whole volume – not even a *slim* volume – an 'Idle' essay, perhaps. Stick to what you are best at, Mr Jerome – give us some more ghost stories: there is always a demand for them.

Yours faithfully,
C. Pooter

Three days later, Pooter wrote one more letter, and then that is the last we hear from him until nearly the end of January. Possibly Jerome's reply, if he ever sent one, withered the chronicler of Brickfield Terrace into silence (there is a sixteen-day gap in the *Diary*, too). More likely, considering that London was about to endure over a fortnight of freezing fogs, so the newspapers of the period record (it is not mentioned in the *Diary*, but then Pooter hardly ever bothered to report the weather), the hiatus is very simply explained by the following:

135

To Messrs The 'EE-ZEE-KOPI' C^{oy},
The Writing Fluid Manufactory,
Pension Street, Hackney, E

Gentlemen –   January 9 '89

As a (hitherto, highly) satisfied owner of an 'Ee-zee-kopi' Model 'B,' I have been experiencing some difficulty with the apparatus during the cold snaps we have been having.

The only room in which I am able to keep my machine, being without any means of heating [this confirms that he must have kept it hidden in a cellar or loft], it is almost like being out-of-doors, when it comes to the temperature. With the coming on of winter, the curved cast-iron arm (Fig. 3 in your instruction booklet) that one pulls down to close the hinged spring-lid (Fig. 4) with force enough to secure the imprint, has been getting stiffer and stiffer, and in frosty weather sometimes jams altogether, responding only to blows from a wooden mallet. This creates a shuddering effect which slightly displaces the inked gelatine bed, with the result that fac-similes come out blurred [as has this one]. Application of a little grease to the arm ball-joint and lid hinges (for want of proper machinery grease, which cannot be bought in small quantities, I have been using lard: and should like to ask, whether this is preferable to beef dripping) eases the stiffening somewhat, but it is still hard to pull down the arm – with consequent aches and pains in *my own*, flesh-and-blood, arm!

That is a nuisance, but I would not pitch it higher – it is what one must expect where there are moving parts (I am told that our scullery mangle has been giving similar trouble), and I am only too thankful that the ironwork has been galvanised against rust. What is more serious, is that your patent oil-based heliotrope ink, without which the apparatus cannot function at all – are we not warned, on a special label, in red letters, never to attempt to use ordinary domestic or commercial inks? – is so susceptible to frost that it freezes as quickly and as easily as milk in a larder. This morning the bottle was solid ice for two inches down – I had to stand it in the hearth for twenty minutes before it would thaw out. This being not always convenient

It is still hard to pull down the arm

[i.e., when Carrie was in the house], I am writing to enquire, whether there is any tried and proven method of preventing the fluid from icing over.

The solution is said to be oil-based, and I had always understood that oil cannot freeze. It follows, therefore, that your laboratory must add some agent – the heliotrope, perhaps – which does make oil freeze. Cannot a further agent be added, which would not affect the ink but which would restore to the oil base its former non-freezing properties?

I note that one of the testimonials in your advertisement in *Whitaker* is from Col. 'Chum' Roper-Fawkes, the celebrated mountaineer and Editor of *Every Boy's Flag Magazine* ('The Flag Mag'). The Colonel does not say in which capacity he uses the apparatus – it is difficult to envisage an 'Ee-zee-kopi' accompanying him upon a mountaineering expedition, altho' it could presumably be stripped down into parts and carried by bearers; but if this popular hero's exploits of 'derring-do' include any first-hand experience of making 'Ee-zee-kopi' fac-similes under icy conditions, it would be instructive to hear of it. Your overseas representatives, also, must have reported on how the special ink responds to foreign climates. Perhaps there is an ingredient which is added for use in cold countries and those with mountainous regions; in which event, should it not be available in the Mother Country? It could be put out in small bottles, labelled ' "Ee-zee-kopi" Ink Solution Cold Weather Additive' – I am sure your many clients, including myself, would be quite happy to pay for it.

Awaiting your reply with interest, I am, &c &c,
C. Pooter

To R^{chd} GOWING Esq., c/o Mr Mendelssohn,
19 Hospital Road, Holloway, N

My dear Gowing,   January 27 '89
I cannot thank you enough for one of the cosiest evenings we can remember. Last night, we blundered through the freezing fog to Hospital Road (getting lost three times, and once ending up in a tennis court), to take up your most kind invitation to supper – only to be told by your landlord, that you had gone to Croydon.

How you got there, when there cannot have been any trains running, is a puzzle. Nevertheless, that our old friend was 'not at home' was self-evident. We therefore traipsed back through the fog, this time getting lost no more than twice, and tripping over a kerb no more than once. Sarah having been given the night off in consequence of our believing ourselves to be dining out, I stoked up the fire again, whilst Mrs P prepared boiled eggs and Bovril, off which we made our supper, as there was nothing else in the house.

As I say, the cosiest of evenings – and we have you to thank for it! After supper, we took a little port – what little we had left, barely half a glass each, but it was too foggy to go out again to the grocer's – when you may be sure that the toast was, 'To Absent Friends'!

Believe me, my dear Gowing, Yrs sincerely,
C. Pooter

FEBRUARY 1889

To:

*Kell Bros, Hair Growers – The Editor,
Holloway Journal – R.P. Diplock Esq., Kell Bros –
Messrs Gripp Ltd, Wholesale Fancy Stationers –
'Mr Carby' of Salt & Tucker – Mr Kirby, Ditto –
Mr Farmerson, Ironmonger.*

FEBRUARY 1889

With the collapse of the Job Cleanands bucket-shop share-pushing firm (*Diary*, February 20), Lupin was once more out in the street, and Charles Pooter found himself again wearily cranking the cast-iron arm of the Ee-zee-kopi machine as he strove to find another position for his by now – in the City at least – well-nigh unemployable offspring.

But this was not to be his only subject for concern in the month of February:

To Messrs KELL BROS,
Hair Growers & Hair Dye Mfrs,
Kell House, High Holborn, WC

Dear Sirs,   February 6 '89

I write in regard to your 'Koko' hair producer and hair restorer, a large bottle of which my wife has given me for my birthday, my hair being slightly thin, weak and dead-looking.

As to the efficacy of the tonic, I can offer no testimonial nor venture any opinion, since I have yet to try it. A mere glance at the label on the bottle – an engraving of a young woman luxuriantly endowed with hair, brushing the same before her looking-glass – is sufficient to show that 'Koko' is a *ladies'* preparation.

My wife, having paid out 4s 6d for the stuff, maintains that it makes no difference – as 'hair is hair,' whether it be men's or women's. I do not have to persuade you gentlemen, whose livelihood depends on your knowledge of all matters hirsute, what manifest nonsense such a contention is. It is like saying that 'fur is fur' – whether it be a seal's or a zebra's. Men's hair looks different from the ladies' because it *is* different. Men grow whiskers and moustachios – women (unless they be freaks) do not.

141

Women grow curls – men, in the general run, do not. Men shave – women do not have to. Women can grow hair all down their backs – men cannot, and would not. And so on and so forth.

No: men's hair, neither in its texture, its properties, and its method of growth, is not the same as women's. That we know. The question remains, nevertheless: would, notwithstanding, a preparation for one be of benefit to the other – in the same way, as my wife would argue, that porridge does good to both genders, for all that their internal organs are not the same? Or could what is beneficial for one be *less* than beneficial – be even *harmful* to, the other – as *I* would argue, like certain pills which women are known by married men to take, but which if they were taken by men themselves, would be of no use to them, and might even prove seriously damaging to the system?

I should be grateful if, in your wisdom, you could act as 'referee' in this amicable disputation, as to who is right and who is wrong, when your adjudication would be taken as final.

Believe me, Gentlemen, I am &c &c,

C. Pooter

To THE EDITOR, The *Holloway Journal*,
Holloway Printeries, Printeries Corner,
Holloway Road, N

Sir,   February 9 '89

The man who would make a fortune should sell umbrellas in the Caledonian Road. Incredible as it may seem, among the profusion of shops, emporia and booths along this busy thoroughfare, there is not one selling umbrellas – as the undersigned, having been caught in the snow squalls of yesterday, knows to his cost.

Yrs &c &c,

'WRINGING WET VIGILANT'

(C. Pooter)

To R. P. DIPLOCK Esq., B.Sc., Chief Analyst,
Messrs Kell Bros, Hair Growers &c,
Kell House, High Holborn, WC

Dear Mr Diplock,   February 10 '89

I am very much obliged to you for your assurances that the 'Koko' hair producer and restorer is as efficacious for men as for women.

Perhaps you would now be so kind as to explain why, such being the case, the Firm of Kell Bros puts itself to the trouble and expense of manufacturing *two* hair restoratives – 'Koko' for the ladies, and 'Kello' for the gentlemen – with all that is entailed in designing and printing separate labels, advertising &c &c, when evidently they must be the same preparation?

I should further like to ask as follows: As 'Koko' (*vide* Press) is world-renowned for preventing the hair *falling out and turning grey*, what is the purpose in Messrs Kell Bros also being *manufacturers of wigs and hair dye?*

Yours faithfully,
C. Pooter

[If Pooter ever showed the reply from Kell Bros' analyst to Carrie, proving her in the right in 'this amicable disputation,' there is no mention of the triumph in her *Diary*.]

To Messrs GRIPP Ltd,
Wholesale Fancy Stationers & Postcard Mfrs,
15 Sweet Lane, Strand, EC

Dear Sirs,   February 14 '89

Last evening, on what might be termed unspoken instructions from my wife – you will know what I mean – I purchased a Valentine, one of your 'Sweet-heart' series, of Messrs Larby, fancy stationers, Zetland Row, Holloway, N, for which I was charged the monstrous sum of 2/9d (yes! – two shillings and ninepence!). It being the last one they had, and the other stationery shops and fancy goods emporia being closed, it was a case of 'take it or leave it.' Had my wife not been so insistent in her hinting, I should most certainly have 'left it,' and walked out of the shop.

Now, I should like to ask you, as respected men of

I was charged the monstrous sum of 2/9d

business, whose picture postcards I have bought many a time, how you can justify such a price, for twopence-worth of quilted sateen, a bit of lace, and a farthing's-worth of cardboard?

Larby's insist that they make next to nothing out of the cards themselves – that they only stock them to oblige their regular customers, who would otherwise go elsewhere, taking their orders for bun-cases, invitation cards &c &c with them – but that nearly the whole of the profit goes to your good selves, Messrs Gripp, being that you are your own wholesalers as well as the actual manufacturers. (Larby's also said, that if I had come earlier in the day I should have had to pay three shillings – that they only brought the price down because it was near closing-time, and they did not want to be left with an unsaleable line on their hands, as nobody buys Valentines after Feb. 13. This I do not lay at your door – I mean Larby's wanting three shillings – as my belief is that the whole of that extra threepence would have gone to them and not to you.)

Allowing that you will have paid out for the verse and for printing, colouring-in and the cost of the envelope, plus overheads, I would judge that this Valentine was manufactured for a shilling, at most. If I am right in my contention, and Larby's 'next to nothing' amounts – let us generously say – to threepence, then the gross profit accruing to your Firm is 120 per centum. I repeat, Gentlemen: how do you defend such extortion?

In replying, I should be obliged if you would refrain from using an envelope embossed with your trademark, since my wife, who only *suspects* that I sent her one of your Valentines, but who must never know for certain, might smell a rat.

Yours &c &c,

C. Pooter

To Mr CARBY, Chief Clerk, Messrs Salt & Tucker,
Share & Stock Brokers,
Barry House, Moorgate Street, EC

Dear Mr Carby,   February 22 '89

I am sure you will not have forgotten how often we used to bump into one another at the South London Athenaeum – twice, I believe; indeed, I *know*, since I have only been twice. Mr Nobbs it was who introduced us – he and I then both lived in Peckham, and I was on both occasions his guest.

I do not have to tell you anything about the shocking failure of Job ('Clean-'em-out') Cleanands and his absconding like that – that scoundrel has brought shame upon the City. It was a double blow to me, since not only did I lose £18 on Parchikka Chlorates which I had bought on what seemed to be good advice, but my son Lupin – known to you as Willie: you will have heard me talk of him, when he was at the Bank at Oldham – had the misfortune to be in the employ of the blackguard, through no fault of his own.

I am now writing to ask you whether you could see your way to using your good offices to enquire whether there might be a place for Lupin at Messrs Salt & Tucker. I am sure he would be an asset to any Firm he worked for, having had better than three months' experience in a brokerage house – albeit a disreputable one, as it has turned out – and being 'keen as mustard' and anxious to 'get on.' Being very much in the 'social swim' in North London, he occasionally earned commission by introducing new clients to Mr Cleanands – one of them, indeed, was a former client of Salt & Tucker, a Mr Chelmsley, whose son is a friend of Lupin's through an amateur dramatic society, 'The Holloway Comedians.' That shows that unlike many City clerks of his age (he is twenty) – we both know the type! – Lupin does not leave his duties when he lays down his pen.

I am quite desperate for him as, when he left the Bank for his health (there is no worry on that score: he is as 'fit as a fiddle' now), he was three months without a position. I would have written to you then, but I had forgotten your name. You know how it is – something is on the tip of your tongue, but you just cannot 'spit it out.' So be a good fellow and do what you can.

Believe me, Yours faithfully,
C. Pooter

To Mr KIRBY, Chief Clerk, Messrs Salt & Tucker
Dear Mr Kirby,   February 22 '89

I had no sooner dropped my letter into the pillar-box than it came to me that your name is not Carby, but Kirby. I was mixing you up with a gentleman we met over at Margate when down at Broadstairs two years ago. I am very sorry – I know how vexatious it can be, having had first-hand experience – that 'rag' the *Blackfriars Bi-weekly News*, in its account of the Lord Mayor's Ball last year (were you there? I didn't see you), referred to me first as 'Porter' then, by way of correction, as 'Pewter.'

146

But if you will read my 'Carby' letter as to your good self, I shall be in your debt.

In haste to catch the last post, Yours f'fully,
C. Pooter

A list of twenty-nine other brokerage houses, evidently copied from the Stock Exchange Year Book, and in half a dozen cases annotated with the name of some employee known to Pooter (e.g., 'Beamish & Gantry, 26 Goose Alley, Fenchurch St – Mr Menzies (? Manzies), Asst(?) Chief Clk)' is pinned to the 'Carby' letter, but as no names are ticked off, there is no way of judging to how many firms Pooter wrote this time round, nor, since he made no Ee-zee-kopi facsimiles, whether these subsequent applications would have stood more or less of a chance than the one to the Chief Clerk of Salt & Tucker. By the absence of any follow-up correspondence we may take it that they all fell on deaf ears. On February 28, however, Pooter was astounded, if not exactly delighted, to receive, out of the blue and completely unsolicited, the offer of a job for Lupin:

To Mr FARMERSON, Ironmonger &c,
18, 19, 20 Percy Row, Holloway, N

Dear Mr Farmerson,   February 28 '89
I was surprised, not to say astonished, to receive your solicitous letter sent over by hand today, for which I thank you. Be it said at once that things are not as bad for us as you have been led to believe they are – by whom, I know not – indeed, my son's temporary misfortune apart, they are not 'bad' in any degree. My losses on Parachikka Chlorates are my own business and nobody else's, but if it is of any interest to you, you may rest assured that they are considerably smaller than rumour would appear to have it. Having been in the City for twenty years and more, I am not such a 'Juggins' as to put all my eggs in one basket!

Turning now to your kind proposition: allow me to say that I do *not* envisage a future in the ironmongery trade for Lupin. That it is an honourable trade I make no doubt. That the ironmonger has an important place in Commerce

147

is beyond dispute – we have only to consider the old adage, that 'for want of a *nail*, the battle was lost.' That it is possible to be both an ironmonger and a gentleman is equally irrefutable – a stevedore, a tramp, may be a gentleman: and were you and I not fellow-guests at the Lord Mayor's Ball last year?

But – I have not brought up my son to be a counter-hand, wrapping up putty and weighing out quarter-pounds of tin-tacks all the live-long day. *That* is not what his schooling has been for, nor what his social position has accustomed him for. You say that there is a grand opportunity for 'a bright lad of his age' – that you are expanding all the time – that you are buying up the bread shop at No. 21 Percy Row and knocking through the wall to make a special new department, selling nothing but wire netting and all things for the poultry yard &c. But did you buy up the whole of Percy Row, Mr Farmerson – and I doubt not that you will – my son, call him under-manager or what you will, would still be a glorified counter-hand; and did we live to see the grand opening of Farmerson's Emporium – as I readily believe we shall – then dress he never so dapperly in frock coat and spats, he would be no more than a floorwalker. I tell you this – that had I wanted *that* for my son, with my influence I could have got him into the Army & Navy Stores.

No, my dear Sir – his future is in the City, where his father's future was, and his father's father's before him. But I thank you most civilly for the offer. The boy who fetches round our coal-bricks from Chelps', the green-grocer's, seems 'a bright lad' – you could do worse than to give him a chance.

There was no need to enclose the reminder that your bill for the last two months is outstanding. It was an oversight – I am very prompt as you know, and our charwoman must have used the bills for lighting the fire, or they would have been paid. As soon as I am able to get to the Bank for the money – I do not like writing out cheques, because of the stamp duty – I will send Sarah across with it.

Yours sincerely,
C. Pooter

MARCH 1889

To:

Marley & Jacobs, Painters & Decorators – Mr Handycross,
'The Firs' – L. Cummings Esq. – Mr Stanley Jacobs,
of Marley & Jacobs – P. Griffin Esq., 'The Larches' –
M. Leach Esq., 'The Hollies' – 'Clarion,' Bicycle News – Rev.
Cecil Dolley, Church Of All Saints – Silas Perkupp Esq. –
G.C. Trout Hartley Esq., MP.

MARCH 1889

From the *Diary* for March 21 we learn that Mr Perkupp was to put to rest his faithful servant's anxieties about his son – if only temporarily – by himself taking Lupin into the office of Perkupp & Co. Another weight off Pooter's mind – though again, not for long – was that Daisy Mutlar married another. Relieved, for the time being, of parental worries, Pooter turned his pen, and the Ee-zee-kopi apparatus, to the more humdrum events of the day – not always, as it proved, to his advantage.

To Messrs MARLEY & JACOBS,
Painters & Decorators,
Tannery Yard, Makepeace Street, Holloway, N

Dear Sirs,   March 2 '89
   Thank you for sending over the tile samples, but I have decided not to half-tile the bathroom just yet after all, but to put up embossed paper half-way with a frieze, painted dark chocolate, and I may give you an order for this later on. Please send back for the tiles if you want them – one of them, the St Joan of Arc at the stake as I think it is, is badly crazed, but that is the condition in which I found it, so I hope you will not think it is any of my doing, as it looks a valuable tile.
   Whilst writing, I wonder if anyone has ever told you that your names, if put in the reverse order then placed together, and dropping the final letter out of the 'Jacobs,' make up the name of the ghost – Scrooge's partner, as was – in *A Christmas Carol* – to wit, Jacob Marley. To add to the coincidence, your premises happen to be in *Makepeace* Street – the middle name of Dickens' principal rival, Thackeray!

Yours, &c &c,
C. Pooter

To Mr HANDYCROSS,
'The Firs,' Brickfield Terrace,
Holloway, N

Dear Mr Handycross,   March 4 '89

When we were introduced by the Vicar last evening, upon your just moving into Holloway from Sawbridge-worth, I did not realise that you had come to live in Brickfield Terrace itself – my maid has just heard it from Borset, the butterman, who, by the bye, comes recommended, except for his eggs – or I should have been more effusive in my welcome.

I trust and believe that you and Mrs Handycross will be content here. You should not miss the country too much, as it is very quiet, and only yesterday I saw a vole, or some such small creature, on the railway embankment. Warmest congratulations upon calling your house 'The Firs.' It is the first case in this street where a house has been given a name, of a tree-like nature, which corresponds in the slightest degree to what is growing in its front garden!

Yours sincerely,
C. Pooter

To L^{eo.} CUMMINGS Esq.,
'Longshanks,' Brickfield Terrace,
Holloway, N

My dear old Cummings,   March 4 '89

We have not seen you for a bit. Upon going through my loft – before the dreaded 'Ides of Spring Cleaning' are upon us!! – I find an accumulation of back numbers of the *Bicycle News* going back to last April, and amounting to some twenty issues or more, which you have kindly sent or brought across from time to time. Would you like them back? You have never said what you would have me do with them, after looking at them. I know, where you have marked them, that many of them contain paragraphs concerning our old friend 'Long' Cummings, as he is known in the bicycling fraternity, and I would have thought you would like these for your scrapbook – or do you perhaps take in two copies? Anyway, if they are not to go to the rag-and-bone man, you had better come and claim them.

As ever, your old friend,

C. Pooter

To Mr HANDYCROSS,

'The Firs,' Brickfield Terrace,

Holloway, N

Dear Mr Handycross,   March 5 '89

Please believe that your suspicions are without foundation and that there was *nothing* sarcastic in my letter of yesterday's date – had I wished to wax satirical, you would have been left in no doubt of it, as many could tell you!

I intended no disparagement of your dwarf conifers, which enhance the Terrace. My point – my simple point – was that, lo and behold!, actual, living firs are to be perceived in the garden of 'The Firs,' whilst larches are not to be seen at 'The Larches,' and whilst 'The Laurels' boasts not laurels but holly bushes, and 'The Hollies,' not hollies but laurels. I hope we shall see you in Church on Sunday, when we may shake hands over this quaint misunderstanding.

Yours sincerely,

Charles Pooter

To Mr Stanley JACOBS, Messrs Marley & Jacobs,

Painters & Decorators, Tannery Yard,

Makepeace Street, Holloway, N

Dear Sir,   March 5 '89

Thank you for your 'congratulations' upon my being the 1,000th person, as you put it, to point out the 'Jacob Marley' connexion. I am sure your satire is worthy of Dickens himself.

It is most certainly *not* my responsibility to send back the tiles to you. They are your tiles: they are here if you want them – but do not wait too long, or you may have to prise them up out of my crazy paving.

I have already told you that the Joan of Arc one was

153

damaged before it got here, and I will go to the stake myself before paying for it, especially such a preposterous amount. Why did you send me a 1/3d tile in the first place? You cannot seriously believe that I would half-tile my bathroom at such a price per tile – especially with so gloomy a subject. Even alternating with the Dutch windmill motif to make a pattern, there would have been approx. 250 Joans of Arc burning at the stake for me to feast my eyes upon while performing my ablutions. What sane man wants that?

Yours sincerely,
C. Pooter

PS I shall be placing the order for embossed paper with Mr Putley, who has served me well in the past.

To P. GRIFFIN Esq.,
'The Larches,' Brickfield Terrace,
Holloway, N

Dear Griffin,   March 10 '89

I am sure I do not know what you mean by 'ridiculous feud.' I am perpetuating nothing – I merely mentioned to the owner of 'The Firs,' out of common politeness to a new neighbour, that his nomenclature is apposite, whereas ours – yes, I include 'The Laurels' – is not. I hope we may shake hands at Church next Sunday.

Yours sincerely,
C. Pooter

To M. LEACH Esq.,
'The Hollies,' Brickfield Terrace,
Holloway, N

Dear Sir,   March 12 '89

Without Prejudice

I do not believe I care for the tone of yours of today's date. There was *no* innuendo in what I wrote to Mr Handycross, who should never have shown you my letter.

I said only what I have already said, or written, to your face – namely, that there are hollies at 'The Laurels,' but no laurels, and laurels at 'The Hollies,' but no hollies. It is a botanical fact – where is the libel in that? I should not speak lightly of litigation – I have powerful friends in the City, should you wish to pursue that line. But I live in hope that we shall hear no more of this tiresome business and that we may shake hands at Church on Sunday.

Yours sincerely,
C. Pooter

To L^{eo.} CUMMINGS Esq.,
'Longshanks,' Brickfield Terrace,
Holloway, N

My dear Cummings,   March 14 '89

My, oh, my, how touchy everybody is, this month! It must be the unseasonable drizzle – it is very miserable, I know, but come! let us be friends.

In the first place, how was I to know that you had gone to Chelmsford for a few days? You did not say – Gowing never told me – and I am not a mind-reader.

In the second, we have been friends long enough for you to know, surely, that I would never use the soubriquet 'old' in any pejorative way. It was a familiar – I hope I am allowed that, after all this time? – address of affection, not a reference to your age at all, and certainly not a 'cruel swipe' at your limp. I did not even know you had acquired a limp – I am sorry that you have – not having seen you, due, as I now realise, entirely to your absence in Chelmsford.

As for those back numbers of the *Bicycle News*, I know that you lay great store by that journal – altho' 'jewel beyond price' is pitching it a little high, to my mind – but I truly thought you must have duplicate copies, else why should you allow me to hang on for so long to those numbers which mention the name of 'Long' Cummings? At any rate, when you did not send across for them in response to my letter, and knowing nothing about your absence in Chelmsford, the top and tail of it is that I sold them as waste-paper. There! It is out, now, old friend – dear friend, I should say. The florin they fetched is yours, naturally. Do not take it to heart – I am sure that they can easily be replaced – just drop a line to the Back Numbers Dept. You never told me that you had a complete run of the *Bicycle News* going back to the day it was founded – it must be a priceless collection.

Why not call round after supper tonight, and tell us what you have been doing in Chelmsford?

As always, Your *old* friend,
C. Pooter

To 'CLARION,' The *Bicycle News*,
Messrs Sir Timothy Diamond Periodicals Ltd,
Diamond House, Farringdon Road, EC

Dear Sir,   March 15 '89

My friend 'Long' Cummings, who I know is no stranger to you as he is often mentioned in your columns, has suggested that I write to you, as I am anxious to lay my hands on copies of the *Bicycle News* for last April 7, 14 and 21, May 5 and 19, June 23, July 7, Sept. 15, 22, 29 (the Bicycles Exhibition Double Number, including the Supplement), October 20, Nov. 17, Dec. 22 (Double 'Xmas Number – coloured plate must be included) and 29; and Jan. 5 and 12 and Feb. 9 (Tandem Number) of this year.

Had your Back Numbers Warehouse not been flooded out after the recent thaw, and all remaining copies of the *Bicycle News*, *Hutch & Perch*, the *Fretworker*, *Our Little Mites' Own*, the *Banjo Player*, the *Health Appliances Advertiser*, *Comicalities*, and *Diamond's Monthly Journal* been reduced to pulp, then I should have had no difficulty in this regard. The deprivation having been suffered, I am compelled to ask you the favour, of finding room in the 'Clarion Calls' page, for a brief paragraph saying that 'Vigilant' of Holloway (the undersigned, address supplied as above) would appreciate the above numbers in good condition, to complete a collection, and would pay a

The urn on the late Mrs Mooney-Kneller's last resting-place
became accidentally dislodged

reasonable price for the same, enquiries to be c/o the *Bicycle News*.

I am, &c &c,

C. Pooter

[This painful episode (see also April 24–25: to Cummings) goes unmentioned in the *Diary*, as does Pooter's altercation with his neighbours (see below). Prudently, perhaps, in what would have been an even more upsetting month had these incidents come to the notice of Carrie, Pooter elected to leave his diary for March completely blank until the 20th.]

To The Rev. Cecil DOLLEY,
The Church Of All Saints, Railway Tunnel Approach, Holloway, N

Dear Rev. Mr Dolley,   March 18 '89

I should like to apologise formally for the scene in the churchyard after the Men's Guild meeting on Sunday, when a discussion with some of my neighbours grew over-heated, and the urn on the late Mrs Mooney-Kneller's last resting-place became accidentally dislodged. I trust my friends at 'The Firs,' 'The Hollies' and 'The Larches' have had the grace to apologise likewise.

Yours most contritely,

C. Pooter

To Silas PERKUPP Esq., Messrs Perkupp & Co.,
Tinkers Rents, Cheapside, EC

My dear Mr Perkupp,   March 21 '89

Words can never

[Given the date, this holograph fragment can only be Pooter's attempt to set down on paper his heartfelt thanks to Mr Perkupp for taking Lupin into the office. The writing is blurred, as if water has been spilled on the paper at some time. It is evidently a rough draft, since it is written on the back of a facsimile routine letter changing a dental appointment (of little interest to the reader), which is why

Cannot you get a law passed, to curb the hurdy-gurdy nuisance?

it survives. There is no evidence of the letter ever having been completed.]

To G.C. TROUT HARTLEY Esq., MP [C., Islington N],
House of Commons, SW

My dear Sir,   March 26 '89

Cannot you get a law passed, to curb the hurdy-gurdy nuisance? Five of them were at it in this street yesterday – a Sunday, the first being at it before seven in the morning. It is like Bedlam – as you, Sir, would know, if you lived in your constituency, and not in the rural tranquillity of Ham!

Yours very sincerely,
C. Pooter

[This is the only recorded example of Pooter writing to his MP. That he did not, on the available evidence, first exhaust all the usual other channels – the police, the Metropolitan Board of Works, the *Holloway Guardian* – suggests that the letter was written in a moment of impetuosity. Perhaps Carrie had been sharp with him, the incessant grinding of the hurdy-gurdy having brought on one of her headaches. Or perhaps, after an unusually fraught month, Pooter had one himself.]

APRIL 1889

To:

Spears, Nape & Rathbone, Stylographic Pen Mfrs –
P. Griffin Esq., 'The Larches' – The Editor,
Daily Telegraph *– Rt Hon. Henry Matthews Esq.,*
QC, MP, Home Secretary – Manager, Randall's Coffee
Rooms – Mr Padge – R. Gowing Esq. – Mrs Lupkin,
of Southend – L. Cummings Esq.

APRIL 1889

After the upsets and abrasions of March, April was a relatively tranquil month, with Lupin keeping what would nowadays be called a low profile, and only minor irritations to disturb the equilibrium of 'The Laurels.'

To Messrs SPEARS, NAPE & RATHBONE,
Stylographic Pen Mfrs, Pen Corner,
Seething Lane, Birmingham

Dear Sirs,   April 13 '89

I have had the singular misfortune to purchase, of Messrs Larkie & Sons, Legal Stationers, Old Bailey, one of your 'Snaperath' Stylographic Pens, advertised in *Diamond's Halfpenny Weekly* as 'made by British workmen, thoroughly reliable, perfect, and simple. Undoubtedly the best writing instrument in the Market.'

After one week's use, I beg leave to refute four out of five of the aforesaid claims – the 'odd man out' being that the 'writing instrument' – you do well not to harp on about it being a *pen* – is made by British workmen. I cannot prove that it is not, but I suspect that it is put together by Chinese coolies.

As for the wretched article being 'thoroughly reliable,' it either spurts ink all over the place, or that fluid refuses to flow at all. The adjective 'perfect' might be more appropriate if the infernal machine did not require to be struck into the palm of the hand to make it write – as it does, and with often disastrous results. As for 'simple' – the only thing *simple* is the poor customer, who is taken in by your puffs and welshed of nine-and-sixpence.

Messrs Larkie have refused point-blank to return my money, saying that it is nothing to do with them, and that I must apply to the manufacturers for satisfaction. This I hereby do. The 'writing instrument' will be despatched c.o.d. upon receipt of your acknowledgement.

Yrs &c &c,

C. Pooter

PS Pray excuse the writer if this letter is illegible. *It is written with a 'Snaperath' Stylographic Pen!*

To P. GRIFFIN Esq.,
'The Larches,' Brickfield Terrace,
Holloway, N

Dear Griffin,   April 14 '89

I am taking the liberty of returning, with sincere thanks, the parcel of bones wrapped in a very interesting page of the *Star*, which you were kind enough to send over with one of your boys this morning. I am sorry I missed him: his unorthodox method of delivery – dropping them over the garden wall – prevented me from rewarding him as I would have liked to.

I am quite sure that the gift was well-meant and that the bones were intended for Mrs Pooter to make stock with, or to boil up into a soup. Mrs Pooter begs me to say that 'she is in no doubt that the bones are nourishing, but that she prefers ones with marrow-fat in them, and these she gets by arrangement with the butcher, but to thank our considerate neighbours all the same.'

It is not for me to say how you should dispose of your bones – we donate ours to the Workhouse – but if you grind them up fine, and scatter them over your garden, the chemicals thereby released will improve your top-soil no end, and enable you to grow something other than weeds.

Yours gratefully,

C. Pooter

To THE EDITOR, *Daily Telegraph*,
141 Fleet Street, EC

Sir,   April 17 '89

For the favour of publication

Last evening, in the pouring rain, upon returning to our home in Holloway from the East Acton Volunteer Ball, my

Most painfully pulled my beard

wife and I were humiliated and insulted by the cabman, who firstly refused to take us farther than the Angel, and then, when I found that I had no money about me – if he would have taken us all the way home, I could easily have borrowed some from my son, had he been in – most painfully pulled my beard.

Sir, this is no isolated example. Many is the time, on the rare occasions when I have been forced to take a cab, that, upon my proffering a perfectly adequate 'tip,' the coin has been spat at and I have been pursued with cries of, 'Pah! Go along with you – take the Brown 'bus in future!'

Is it not time, Sir, that there were strict regulations to govern the behaviour of those surly louts, the London cabmen? I propose that they should be put under Government control, and be made answerable in law. Any outraged or insulted fare should be able to *demand*, as of right, to be driven to a magistrate or justice of the peace, that instant, whatever the hour of day or night, when his grievance would be heard, and redress got from the offending cabman.

I am, Sir, yours &c &c,
'VIGILANT' (C. Pooter)

[The regulation demanded by 'Vigilant' in fact already existed. The 'Laws Relating to Hackney Carriages in London' stated: 'In case of any dispute . . . the hirer may require the driver to drive to the nearest Metropolitan Police Court or Justice Room, when the complaint may be determined by the sitting magistrate without summons; or if no Police Court be open at the time, then to the nearest Police Station, where the complaint shall be entered.' His eyes perhaps watering from the beard-pulling ordeal, Pooter, who evidently took cabs rarely, could not have observed that a notice to this effect was posted up in the cab, as required by law.]

To The R^t H$^{on.}$ Henry MATTHEWS Esq., QC, MP,
Principal Secretary of State for Home Affairs,
Whitehall, SW

Sir – April 17 '89
I have the honour to enclose a fac-simile of a letter

which I have this day submitted to the Editor of the *Daily Telegraph*, the subject of which will be self-evident.

So many Members of Parliament must take cabs regularly, to get from their Clubs or places of business to the House, and vice versa, that a 'London Hackney Cabs (Regulation Of)' Bill would surely be read unopposed.

If Parliament concerned itself with the best interests of the Population, instead of the tomfoolery of the Channel Tunnel, then we should all sleep more soundly in our beds.

I have the honour to be, Sir,

Your obedient servant,

C. Pooter

[Ministers and MPs are nowadays snowed under the unwanted photostats of letters submitted to newspapers by angry constituents. Thanks to the miracle of the Ee-zee-kopi apparatus Pooter may have been the first person to commit this particular nuisance against a Home Secretary.]

His traumatic cab-ride aside, the East Acton Volunteer Ball mentioned in the *Daily Telegraph* letter was not the happiest of experiences for Pooter. Having been given tickets by Gowing, he and Carrie arrived at the Drill Hall in the belief that they were guests of the Regiment. Pooter was horrified, after pressing hospitality upon total strangers (including a Mrs Lupkin who invited the Pooters to stay with her in Southend – see April 23 below), to receive a bill for £3 0s 6d, which he could not entirely pay (hence his difficulties with the cabman). The night's embarrassment is preserved, as in aspic, on the gelatine bed of the Ee-zee-kopi.

To THE MANAGER,

Randall's Coffee Rooms & Wedding Breakfast

Supplies &c,

11 & 13 Lower High Street, Acton, W

Dear Sir,   April 17 '89

I enclose a draft for 9/– (nine shillings) in respect of the unpaid portion of my bill at the East Acton Volunteer Ball last evening, and would thank you for accommodating me in this matter.

In order to avoid future misunderstandings of this sort,

167

may I suggest that, when supplying the catering at functions where it has not previously been made clear to the 'guests,' that they are *not* guests at all, but paying customers, you put up a tariff where everyone can see it, clearly giving the prices of the refreshments available.

If I may say so, a special and separate notice, in big letters, to the effect that you charge no less than 11s 6d a bottle for champagne, would certainly have been appreciated, last evening, by –

Yours faithfully,
C. Pooter

To Mr PADGE [an acquaintance],
c/o R^{chd} Gowing Esq., c/o Mr Mendelssohn,
19 Hospital Road, Holloway, N

Dear Padge,   April 17 '89

I do not know your address, and so am asking Gowing to forward this.

It was agreeable to see you again at the Volunteer Ball last evening, after all this time. We enjoyed it very much. As you were in uniform, I expect you must be familiar with 'the form' at these military functions, and would know that the refreshments in the supper room had to be paid for. By the time our bill came, you had escorted the ladies into the dancing-room, and so I could not ask you for your half, and later you were nowhere to be found. It came to £3 0s 6d. The odd sixpence is for the cigar that you had, where I did not; and so if you will send me a postal order or money draft for 30/6d, at your convenience, that will make us 'straight,' and I shall be obliged.

Yours faithfully,
C. Pooter

To R^{chd} GOWING Esq., c/o Mr Mendelssohn,
19 Hospital Road, Holloway, N

My dear Gowing,   April 19 '89

I am sure I don't know what you mean by 'using your rooms as a Post Office.' Is it such an imposition? – when all you had to do was scribble Padge's address on the

168

envelope and re-post it. Very well: I should have asked your *permission* before sending the letter c/o your address. Yes – and I could counter that *you* should have asked *my* permission before bringing Padge to my house that time – *and* I could go on to complain of 'using *my* rooms as an Hotel' – but I shall not be so petty. Now be a good fellow and send me Padge's address, if you won't forward the letter. He owes me 30/6d, which is no small sum, I don't mind telling you.

By the bye, you might have warned me that the Volunteer Ball was a 'paying affair.'

Yours sincerely,
C. Pooter

[Beneath this, Pooter has added an exasperated manuscript note: 'Doesn't know where he lives. Why couldn't he have said so in the first place?']

To Mrs LUPKIN,
'Ozone Villa,' Semaphore Street,
Southend-on-Sea, Essex

Dear Mrs Lupkin,   April 23 '89

After being privileged to entertain you to that delightful champagne supper we all so enjoyed at the Volunteer Ball, it was very nice to receive yours of yesterday, confirming that you would like us to come down and stay with you.

Whilst we often receive kind invitations from friends and acquaintances that we have met at parties, to come and stay with them, I am bound to say that none of them has ever been so generous as to offer to 'charge us half what we would have to pay at the Royal' – or any other hotel, come to that. Mostly, indeed, our friends, when inviting us, don't mention *charges* at all – preferring, I suppose, that we should pay what we like, or, so as to avoid embarrassment all round, that we should not pay at all.

But all that is by the bye. I write to say that, my wife being indisposed, we have, after all, to decline your kind invitation.

Yours sincerely,
C. Pooter

169

The three pounds and sixpence for suppers, ices and champagne at the Volunteer Ball was not Pooter's only untoward expense in April. On the 24th, Pooter brought to a conclusion what must have been a chilly period in his friendship with Cummings (the *Diary* has his usually constant visitor calling only once in April: on the 20th, when he makes a pointed reference to the *Bicycle News*) with the following jellygraphed olive branch:

To L^{eo.} CUMMINGS Esq.,
'Longshanks,' Brickfield Terrace,
Holloway, N

My dear Cummings,   April 24 '89
   I am sending you a fac-simile of a Memo from the Market Book Stall, Blanche Lane Market, Lewisham, offering all the back numbers you want at threepence apiece, buyer collects. It seems pretty steep to me, but it is the only reply I have got, so I suppose 'beggars can't be choosers.' As it is not very convenient for me to go to Lewisham just now – it would take half a day, and I am in the middle of sawing up a big quantity of wood for the fire – would you mind cycling over and getting the magazines, and I will pay for them? You will know then, if they are worth buying.

Yours sincerely,
C. Pooter

[Postcard]

Dear Cummings –   April 25 '89
   Very well – I will go. Sorry, I didn't know your leg was still troubling you. As you say, if they are not 'up to scratch,' I can always take them back.

C.P.

MAY 1889

To:

*E. Finsworth Esq., Deputy Town Clerk of Middlesborough –
Mr Franching, of Peckham – Silas Perkupp Esq. –
G. Crowbillon Esq., of Crowbillon Hall – Messrs Gylterson,
Sons & Co. – Gertie Flack, Laundress.*

While Pooter's satirical letter to Mrs Lupkin (April 23) touching on his and Carrie's 'many kind invitations to stay' may have been exaggerated, socially the Pooters were certainly very much in demand during the Spring, with no fewer than two engagements flooding in. One (*Diary*, April 27–28) was an invitation from an old school friend, one Teddy Finsworth, who had risen to become Deputy Town Clerk of Middlesborough, to have dinner with an uncle of his in Muswell Hill. Neither Pooter's acceptance nor his 'bread-and-butter' thank-you notes to uncle and/or nephew survive, but on May 1 he was writing:

> To E. FINSWORTH Esq., Dep^y Town Clerk,
> The Town Hall, Middlesborough, Yorks
>
> Dear Finsworth,   May 1 '89
>   I have at last remembered the name of the teacher with the white hair who took us for the woodwork class – it has kept me awake ever since your Uncle's dinner. It was *Carpenter*! With such a name, how could we ever have forgotten?
>
> In haste,
> Yrs, Pooter

> [Postcard]
>   May 4 '89
>   You are perfectly right – it was Mr Joyner. Whyever did I think it was Carpenter?
>
> In haste,
> C.P.

On May 10, the Pooters received an important invitation from Mr Franching, of Peckham, to dine with him that very night, to meet Hardfur Huttle, a celebrated American journalist and man of letters. Franching did not attempt to disguise that they would be filling in for two guests who had dropped out at the last minute. Pooter replied at once by telegram:

FRANCHING ESQ STONEQUARRY TERRACE PECK-HAM. WITH PLEASURE STOP IS IT FULL DRESS [The telegram is unsigned. The *Diary* notes: 'By leaving out our name, just got the message within the sixpence [for twelve words].']

To Silas PERKUPP Esq., Messrs Perkupp & Co.,
Tinkers Rents, Cheapside, EC

My dear Mr Perkupp,   May 11 '89

I am very sorry indeed to say that for the second time in his service with Messrs Perkupp & Co. [and the first in twenty years, notes Carrie's *Diary*], your faithful and diligent servant does not feel well enough to come down to the Office this morning. I went out to dinner last evening, to Peckham, with Mr Franching, to meet no less a personage than Mr Hardfur Huttle, when I fear that I ate some poisoned lobster. I promise, my dear Master, this will *not* become habitual – I shall eat no more shell-fish from now on – and will try to get up and come to the Office this afternoon, even though it is a Saturday, and stay until I have caught up with my work. With my deepest and most sincere apologies for putting you to such an unpardonable inconvenience.

Your humble servant,
C. Pooter

[Without any exposition, this letter would raise the question, if Pooter was ill in bed, who, then, made the Ee-zee-kopi facsimile? The answer is that it is not a facsimile at all – it is a fair copy, made in his own hand before – it has to be imagined – giving the original to Lupin to take down to the office. Either Charles Pooter thought his excuse note ought to be on record, or he was very bored lying in bed with an ice pack on his head.]

To S. FRANCHING Esq.,
'Four Gables,' Stonequarry Terrace,
Peckham, SE

My dear Mr Franching,   May 12 '89

I now am feeling well enough to write and thank you, as adequately as I may, for your exquisite hospitality on Friday evening, and for the illustrious company at Dinner, with some brilliant talk. I should have written at once, but I have been laid low with food poisoning, happily now gone. Mrs Pooter also enjoyed herself thoroughly, and told me later that 'she did not feel nearly as terrified as she thought she might.' I call that a tribute to you, for putting her at her ease.

Should you be seeing Mr Hardfur Huttle again, I wonder if I might prevail upon you to pass on a remark of mine, *à propos*. It was when Mr Huttle said, to the company at large, I fancy, altho' addressing your good self in person as his host, 'What we want' – (I wrote all this down on my cuff) – 'in America, is your homes. *We* live on wheels,' and so on and so on. Mr Huttle was in full flow, and it would have been rude to interrupt, but I did want to put in: 'Ah! But my dear Sir! Now, if we could put *our* homes on *your* wheels, then we should all live in caravans, like the Romanies!' I did murmur the interjection as an aside to my neighbour, the charming Mrs Field, hoping that she would pass it on, but I believe she is stone hard of hearing, and so my little sally was lost, which I call a pity. I should like it to have a wider audience.

By the bye, I never got the chance to ask – is your waiter (who I must say was very professional) a Mr Steen, by any chance? I could almost swear he is the same person as the former Secretary of State for the Colonies in the Peckham Mock Parliament – but it is a long time since I was there, so I could be mistaken.

Yours faithfully,
C. Pooter

On that note, the Ee-zee-kopi's breezy chronicle of the Pooters' crowded social life comes to an abrupt stop, its

I wrote all this down on my cuff

gelatine bed no longer having heliotrope ink to spare for frivolities. For the very next day, tragedy struck. Having been with Perkupp & Co. for all of two months, Lupin Pooter was called into Mr Perkupp's private office and summarily discharged. It was to transpire (*Diary*, May 13) that while Pooter was on his post-Franching sickbed the previous Saturday, and Mr Perkupp also being away from the office, Lupin had contrived to lose the firm's most valued client, Mr Crowbillon, by recommending him – Crowbillon being dissatisfied with the service he was getting from Perkupp's – to take his custom to a 'go-ahead' brokerage house known to Lupin, the firm of Gylterson, Sons & Co. Ltd.

Having sent Lupin packing, Perkupp then called in Charles Pooter and instructed him to take himself off home and put together a careful, and by implication cringing, letter to Crowbillon, saying whatever he could to win their treasured client back. Pooter, leaving instructions that he was not to be disturbed even by Cummings or Gowing, hastened to his master's bidding – but not until he had written piteously to Perkupp himself.

To Silas PERKUPP Esq.,
'White Gates,' Kite Hill, Hampstead, NW
My dear Mr Perkupp,   May 13 '89
    I embolden myself to write you at your private address, as I would not wish this letter to be put in the filing cabinet at the Office, for all to see.

    Pained, wronged Master: there are some fathers, after what has happened, who would say, 'Would my son had never been born!' or 'Would that he had been born a girl!' I love my son in spite of everything, and cannot, *will* not, say such things. What I *may* say and *will* say is, that rather than have this Thing befall you, I would sooner have had him go on the stage – emigrate to Canada – become, as he might have done in another station in life, apprenticed to an ironmonger – anything but bring ill-luck upon the House of Perkupp.

    I am truly sorry for what the foolish, headstrong boy has done, and will strive all day and all night with my letter to

Mr Crowbillon, composing it twenty, thirty, fifty times if need be, until I have got it right. I understand that it must *not* look as if my good Master has anything to do with it. With my heart full of woe, I turn now to that duty, in the hope that the harm that has been done, by my own flesh and blood, may yet be undone.

Your remorseful and sorrowing humble, but ever faithful servant, C. Pooter

To Gilbert E. Gillam O. CROWBILLON Esq.,
Crowbillon Hall, Nedgeworth,
by Tapstop St Michael's, Essex

My dear Mr Crowbillon,   May 14 '89

I take pen in hand to correct the foolish misunderstanding which arose when you came into the Office on Saturday, when the Principal was not there to receive you, and the Senior Staff were across at Skeeting's taking their coffee.

The junior clerk who came forward, who I regret to say is my son, should have run across the road and got Mr Davidge or Mr Spotch. Instead, upon hearing that 'this time, this stick-in-the-mud Firm has really got my goat,' and not realising, being new, that you make that announcement practically every time you come – that it has become a 'standing joke' between us (as I'm sure you know it has – one of our clerks, the young scalawag Pitt, does a satirical imitation of your 'stick-in-the-mud' observations, blowing out his cheeks and thumping the day ledger) – upon thinking you seriously meant to withdraw your valued custom, I say, my son stupidly took it upon himself to recommend some fly-by-night, flibberty-gibberty, bucket-shop firm he must have read about in 'Square Miler's' column in the *Evening Argus*, to wit, Gylterson, Sons & Co. Ltd.

Lupin, as my boy is known, has a very thin skull – the doctor at Peckham General used to say it was like an egg-shell – which at some time, during his late childhood, must have suffered a sharp blow or rap, for ever since he has been subject to

Blowing out his cheeks and thumping the day ledger

There ends the first page of the Crowbillon letter, and there are no continuation sheets following, for all Pooter's boast in the *Diary* (May 15) that he composed 'sixteen pages, closely written.' Surprisingly, there are no earlier drafts, either, though the letter must surely have been re-worked 'twenty, thirty, fifty times if need be' – probably more.

In the event, Crowbillon showed as scant regard for the original of Pooter's lengthy missive as Mrs Birrell must have done for the remainder of the facsimile. He replied in 'less than sixteen lines' to the effect that Lupin had displayed more intelligence in five minutes than the firm of Perkupp & Co. had in five years. There the correspondence lapses.

But there was a sequel:

To Messrs GYLTERSON, SONS & CO.,
Leather Buildings, Sweetbread Lane, EC

Gentlemen –   May 16 '89

I am obliged to you for your letter of yesterday's date, with its generous offer of an absolute engagement at a commencing salary of £200 a year, but I fear that I am too old a dog to

Here this manuscript letter breaks off, Pooter obviously just having realised that the letter was addressed not to him, but to Lupin.

For the rest of the month, the clanking arm of the Ee-zee-kopi machine seems to have fallen discreetly silent – until the very last day of May, when Pooter was goaded into penning 'a stern letter . . . very satirical' to the laundress:

To Gertie FLACK,
No. 4 Back Basement,
Sir Transom Showers Homes For The Industrious Poor,
Arcadia Street, Lower Holloway, N

Madam –   May 31 '89

Among last week's laundry you took away three handkerchiefs. You have returned the handkerchiefs without the colour. Perhaps you will return either the colour or the value of the handkerchiefs.

– C. Pooter

Carrie records in her *Diary*: 'He was so pleased with his composition, which he read over many times with a smirk on his face, that I had not the heart to tell him that the laundress cannot read.'

JUNE/JULY 1889

To:

Brawn & Chadwick, 'The Duplicator People' –
O. Branch Esq., Great Northern Railway –
Messrs R. & R. Cargle, Oilmen – The Ee-zee-kopi Co. –
Lupin Pooter – Reprograph Ltd (Successors to
The Ee-zee-kopi Co.) – The Editor, Exchange & Mart

Letters for June are sparse. It may have been that a protracted visit by Mrs James, of Sutton, who introduced the Pooters to the craze for spiritualism and table-rapping (*Diary*, June 1 *et seq.*) left little time for composition. What is more likely is that Pooter was becoming much more selective in his use of the Ee-zee-kopi machine. The following, it will prove, is of the utmost significance in the Pooter archive:

To Messrs BRAWN & CHADWICK,
'The Duplicator People,' Phoenix House,
Glasshouse Street, Stoke-on-Trent, Staffs
Gentlemen –   June 12 '89
From the label pasted in the lid of my 'Ee-zee-kopi' facsimile apparatus, which I purchased second-hand over a year ago, I gather that you are Sole Distributors for the device. I am writing to enquire, whether you are also the Sole Distributors for the special ink solution required, also the special copying paper, as I am experiencing some difficulty in obtaining fresh supplies of the same.

Could you either, kindly quote me a price for a large bottle of the ink and one half-ream of the paper; or furnish me with a list of London stockists, from whom I may order, and oblige –
Yours &c &c,
C. Pooter

To O. BRANCH Esq., Asst Secretary,
The Great Northern Railway, Rocket Chambers,
Great Northern Hotel, Kings X, N
Dear Mr Branch,   June 17 '89
It is very nice to hear from you again, and to have your assurances that the delay in completing the work at the

marshalling yards, due to the amount of sludge that has to be carted away before the track-laying can commence, is now nearly remedied, and that it will not be many months now before the goods trains cease to be diverted past our garden (tho' my wife emphatically does *not* regard them as a *'diversion'*!!).

Thank you also for your courtesy in formally asking our consent for an unobtrusive semaphore signal pole at the bottom of our garden, to be connected with the signal-box at the coal yards. Since, as you say, you are allowed under the Railway and Canal Act to erect signal poles wherever you choose (provided, I would imagine, that they be next to a railway line!), it is very good of you to be so polite. I am returning the form duly signed, accepting the pepper-corn rent (I do not suppose it is an *actual* peppercorn?!). Could you let me know the name of the gentleman who will come to oil the signal, if it makes too much of a noise when changing?

Yours very sincerely,
C. Pooter

PS I have only just noticed that you are Mr O. Branch. It would be incredible if you were a Mr *Olive*(r) Branch!

Dear Mr Branch,   June 20 '89
Thank you very much for letting me know that your name is Mr Oswald Branch. How disappointing! I have made a note of Mr Brindley's name, at the coal yards, and will certainly never try to oil the railway signal myself.

Yours sincerely,
C. Pooter

To Messrs R. & R. CARGLE, Oilmen,
23 Workhouse Hill, Upper Holloway, N

Dear Sirs,   July 4 '89
I have in mind to varnish my floor surrounds, bannisters, stair-tread margins, some doors, and other woodwork. Could you send me a man down to measure up, and give me a quotation for how much varnish I should need?

184

I should also like to know whether, using clear varnish, it is all right to varnish over the existing paintwork, as I have had an unhappy experience with paint stripper. Finally, as it will be a costly business I should think, and I should only want to buy one tin at a time, could you assure me that you will have enough in stock, and are not going to run out of that particular shade of varnish half-way through?

Yours sincerely,
C. Pooter

To Messrs The 'EE-ZEE-KOPI' C^{oy},
The Writing Fluid Manufactory,
Pension Street, Hackney, E

Gentlemen –   July 5 '89

In January last, you were kind enough to give me some advice over the trouble I was having, in making my 'Ee-zee-kopi' apparatus work in the cold weather, and with the special ink solution freezing over. I am sorry never to have acknowledged your helpful letter, but I accidentally spilled some brown sauce over the signature, and so knew not whom to write to.

You will be pleased to know that keeping the ink in a warm place, as you suggested, was effective in stopping it from freezing; and that a sock, placed over the cast-iron arm which operates the hinged lid, was equally efficacious.

I now presume to intrude upon your patience further, in the hope that you will be as helpful as you were before. My difficulty now is that I am running out of the special paper and special ink solution, and am experiencing difficulty in obtaining fresh supplies.

I wrote to your Sole Distributors, Brawn & Chadwick, at Phoenix House, Stoke-on-Trent, but the letter has been returned by the Post Office, marked 'Factory burned down – no forwarding address.' Am I to take it that Brawn & Chadwick have gone out of business? If not, I wish you would tell me where they are to be found now-a-days. If they have 'given up the ghost,' have you appointed other Sole Distributors, and could you oblige me with their address?

A sock was equally efficacious

I know that the materials I require are not available at ordinary stationer's, because I have tramped up and down the Strand enquiring at one after the other. Some of them were quite rude. Merryweather's professed never to have heard of the 'Ee-zee-kopi;' Chaps & Dell tried to fob me off with common duplicating paper and ordinary ink, which they swore would not harm the works at all; and Zimmerman's – as if it were any of their business – said that if I only wanted to make one copy at a time, why did I not hire a type-writer (for 15/– a month, if you please!) and invest in a quire of carbonic paper? As for Jagger's, the stupid shop-hand swore you had gone out of business!

If, by any chance, you yourselves, as manufacturers, are able to supply me with ink solution in the large bottle, and half a ream of the copying papers, then I should be perfectly willing to pay the retail price. Hoping for the favour of a speedy reply, as I am getting rather low,

Yours, &c &c,

C. Pooter

To Messrs R. & R. CARGLE, Oilmen,
23 Workhouse Hill, Upper Holloway, N

Dear Sirs,   July 7 '89

What a rude letter! I know perfectly well that *clear* varnish does not come in different shades – but *you*, as Oilmen, must know perfectly well that one make of clear varnish is not the same as another. They are indefinably different.

Do not bother to send a man down after all. I shall take my business to Putley's.

Yours sincerely,

C. Pooter

PS I said nothing about wanting to purchase the varnish on the three years' system. I would have bought what I needed by the week, for spot cash.

Towards the end of June, Lupin, declaring Brickfield Terrace to be a bit 'off' as good addresses went (the railway signal at the bottom of the garden, according to Carrie's *Diary* entry for June 29, was the last straw) had moved to Bayswater, to be near his friends, the hat manufacturer Murray Posh and his wife, the former Daisy Mutlar. Having come to the opinion that, considering she was now a married lady, Lupin was being overly familiar with Mrs Posh (in fact he was about to get engaged to Posh's sister), Pooter sat down on July 10 to write him 'a long letter . . . feeling it my duty to do so.'

To Lupin POOTER Esq.,
A^{pt} C, No. 6 Blackfield Gardens, Bayswater, W

My dear Boy,   July 10 '89

How like the old times when you were at Oldham, it feels, sitting down to write to you at your rooms (which

187

thankfully are in Black*field* Gardens, and not 'Black *Lion*' Gardens, nor 'Black *Horse*' Gardens, nor 'Black *Bull*' Gardens!). There is a salient difference, however – that now, but a month off your majority, and settled in a substantial position at Messrs Gylterson's (of which we are very proud), you are an older, wiser man.

But stay! An older, wiser man, that is to say – except in one regard (I mean as to being wiser, not of course as to being older, where an exception would be an impossibility), and that is in your attention to Mrs Posh, on which I must – I *shall* – speak my mind.

My boy, when your Ma and I dined with you and the Poshes and Miss Posh at your apartments, I am bound to say that the familiar way in which you addressed that lady – Mrs Posh, I mean to say, 'though Miss Posh no less so – was – I will not mince words – quite repreh

Here, in mid-word, we come to the end of the page. There is no accompanying continuation sheet, but on the back of the tissue-like copying paper on which this facsimile has been made, there is a mass of heliotrope smudges, suggesting an unsuccessful effort at reproducing the letter on both sides of the paper. The reason for this attempted economy, if not already apparent from the July 5 letter to the Ee-zee-kopi Company, becomes crystal clear when we read:

To Messrs 'REPROGRAPH' Ltd
(Successors to the 'Ee-zee-kopi' C^{oy} Ltd),
301 Doris Road, Shadwell, E

Dear Sirs,   July 10 '89
I have to thank you for your amazing letter of yesterday's date, in reply to mine which had been forwarded to you from the former Writing Fluid Manufactory in Pension Street, Hackney. The fact that the 'Ee-zee-kopi' factory is now an antiseptic skin soap warehouse is a matter of absolute indifference to me. What *is* of interest, and greatly so, is that Messrs 'Ee-zee-kopi' having gone out of business, or more accurately, been bought out by you, who then cease all production of the 'Ee-zee-kopi' apparatus (why, then, it is pertinent to ask, did you want

188

to buy it in the first place?), you are calmly proposing to dishonour the obligations which that firm – now your firm – had – *has* – to each and every one of its customers.

Gentlemen: along, I dare say, with tens of thousands of others, I purchased my 'Ee-zee-kopi' machine in good faith, in the confident belief that manufacture of the special ink solution and copying paper required to work the apparatus, would continue in perpetuity. Without these materials, the 'Ee-zee-kopi' is so much scrap iron, whose gelatine bed may as well be melted down for candles.

I have thrown your insulting illustrated leaflet on the fire. I emphatically do *not* wish to buy a 'Reprograph' auto-copying machine, whether for eight guineas cash, or on 'easy terms,' however superior *you* may regard it to the 'out-moded,' and 'primitive' 'Ee-zee-kopi' device. That it will provide countless copies, on ordinary paper, leaves me unmoved. I do not desire countless copies, I require but one copy. For this purpose, I *must* have the special ink solution and copying paper, that goes with the 'Ee-zee-kopi' apparatus. This need is now imperative, since I am now down to a teaspoonful of the former, and my last two sheets of the latter.

Pray send me, without delay, the name and address of the firm of scrap merchants who carted away the remaining stocks of these important materials from the 'Ee-zee-kopi' manufactory.

This letter is without prejudice to any legal action which I may take against you, to recover the cost of my now useless fac-simile machine.

Yours &c &c,
C. Pooter

To THE EDITOR, Exchange & Mart,
170 Strand, London, WC

Sir –   July 11 '89

I wish to nominate for your 'Black Book' Department, in which you warn readers of former advertisers with your esteemed journal who have proved themselves to be rogues, the name of Messrs 'Reprograph' Ltd (Successors to the 'Ee-zee-kopi' C^{oy} Ltd), of Doris Road, Shadwell, E.

Sir, in the current issue of the *Exchange & Mart* I have counted up no fewer than three second-hand 'Ee-zee-kopi' fac-simile machines for sale. Each advertisement makes much of the fact that 'roller, ink and copying papers' are included in the price. What none reveals, the ink being special ink and the copying paper special paper, is that (in all fairness, the advertisers may not know this, though I have a good idea that the one offered at '10/– for quick sale or w.h.y.,' is not in ignorance of the situation) when whatever may be sold with the apparatus is gone, there is no more to be had, since the 'Ee-zee-kopi' firm has gone out of business, and its successors have consigned its stocks to the scrapyard.

Sir, let my last 'Ee-zee-kopi' fac-simile, made with my last drop of 'Ee-zee-kopi' ink, upon my last sheet of 'Ee-zee-kopi' copying paper, be of this earnest appeal to your readers, to have nothing whatsoever to do with

Here the writing becomes an illegible, watery blur. It continues for another five and a half lines before then becoming no more than a faint heliotrope smudge, which then fades away altogether. Thus, in this cry from the heart to the *Exchange & Mart*, ends the last recorded letter of Charles Pooter, of 'The Laurels,' Brickfield Terrace, Holloway, N.